B A B E L

new writing | introduced by
ANDREW MOTION

A CCPA paperback

BABEL

First published in Great Britain 1999.

ISBN 0 9536072 0 8

Typeset in Palantino.

Printed and bound in Great Britain by
Biddles Ltd., Guildford, Surrey.

Acknowledgements

Babel is grateful to The Centre for Creative and Performing Assistance for its generous financial assistance.

Many thanks also to Jon Cook, Andrew Motion, Andy and Vanessa Vargo, Phoebe Phillips, Vicky Winteringham, Mike Oates, Anastacia Tohill at the Norwich School of Art and Design, Julia Bell, Bill Bigge, Julian p Jackson, Val Striker and Aileen Davies.

The *Babel* Team:
Karen Goodwin, Tim Guest, Nicole Linhardt, Damon Mullins and Johnny Rich.

Cover design:
Caroline Tomlinson

CONTENTS

ANDREW MOTION

Introduction

This anthology is the eleventh in a series edited, designed and published by members of the Creative Writing MA group at the University of East Anglia and contains work they have produced during the first two-thirds of their year-long course. As with previous anthologies, the intention is to gain a wider audience for the students' writing than can be found within the university; the effect is to prove, once again, the dynamism and distinction of the whole project.

Two years ago, for the first time, a poetry course was included as a part of the MA, running parallel to the much longer-established course prose course (set up by Malcolm Bradbury and Angus Wilson in 1970). Poems are now an important feature of the anthology – and they complement its other kinds of exploration. The book contains a multiplicity of voices, speaking in a wide range of styles and idioms, and reflects an enormous breadth of backgrounds and interests. There are poems, prose and drama by students from all over the UK and as far afield as Bangladesh, the US and the Ivory Coast. There are short stories and novel extracts written in a familiar realistic manner and others which are experimental; there are comedies as well as tragedies; there are candid strong feelings and there are ingenious ironies. This variety is essential to the health of the course, as well as our pleasure in reading the work that arises from it.

Over the years, the MA has gained a reputation for turning out writers who have successful literary careers. Ian McEwan and Kasuo Ishiguro, both Booker Prize winners, are our best known graduates. More recently, very distinguished books have been published by Martin Bedford, Stephen Foster and Elizabeth Ridley; Phil Whitacker won the John Llewellyn Rhys Prize for his first novel; and Sarah Corbett was shortlisted for the

Forward Poetry Prize and the T. S. Eliot Prize for her first collection of poems. In 1999 alone, no fewer than eight books will be published by recent graduates of the course – and there are others already set to come out in 2000.

These are heartening facts – but if they give the impression that the course is a kind of conveyor belt, designed to turn out publishable manuscripts, they are misleading. The point about the course is not that it concentrates first and foremost on impressing literary agents, nor on getting published – significant as these things are – but that it puts the act of writing before everything else in the minds of its students. It offers a time for self-discovery and self-definition, for exploration and mutual encouragement – above all, a time for concentration on creation.

This is why the point about variety is so important. The range and open-mindedness of the anthology shows that everyone in it is completely engaged with being themselves for the benefit of their readers. The quality of the work that it contains and its unflagging spirit of adventure makes it a worthy sequel to its distinguished predecessors.

Tim Ashwell

Toast

Tim Ashwell (formerly Glover) had his first two plays, *All the World's a Biscuit* and *Not Enough Points on the Chicken*, presented at the National Student Drama Festival; the former winning the originality award.

He is currently working on a newly devised piece to be presented at The Edinburgh Festival. He is also working on a number of screenplays and making tentative steps towards a career in stand-up comedy.

His first full-length play, *Expecting Rain*, is currently 'in a drawer'.

LORENZO *is pacing his front room looking anxious. Enter* DOC *in immaculate, tight-fitting, blue overalls. He looks as spotless as a T.V. KwikFit-Fitter and has the air of authority of a brain surgeon. He carries a mysterious, box-like package concealed by a green surgical cloth and has a large array of screwdrivers peeking out of his breast pocket.*

LORENZO   What's the verdict, Doctor? Can I call you doctor, doctor?

DOC *puts down the package carefully. He answers in his own time with his usual deliberate precision.*

DOC   Call me Doc.
LORENZO   (*Fuelled by a nervous energy*) So what's the score, Doc?
DOC   There is no score, Mr. Lorenzo. This isn't a game.
LORENZO   Tell it to me straight, is it good or bad?
DOC   I don't use those terms.
LORENZO   (*Cracking his calm veneer*) For God's sake! How is she?
DOC   (*Controlled*) Different.
LORENZO   (*Getting angry, losing control*) DIFFERENT? How 'different'? What the fuck does different mean?
DOC   (*Covering the package as if to protect its ears*) Hold your tongue, Mr. Lorenzo. Don't get tetchy! I can understand your concern, but what you must realise is that what we need to establish here is a state of calm. Now please sit down.
LORENZO   (*Still standing*) So it's serious?
DOC   Any situation of this magnitude is serious.

Lorenzo	Magnitude! What are you telling me?
Doc	(*Authoritative*) I'm telling you to sit down and calm down.
Lorenzo	Calm down? How am I supposed to calm down when you start using words like 'serious' and 'magnitude'...?
Doc	I'm sorry if my language offends you. Now I assure you that I will do my utmost to tone down the severity of the situation and the horrific facts at my disposal... (*In the same breath*) ...Mr. Lorenzo, you appear to be upstanding. (LORENZO *sits.*)
Lorenzo	Just tell me, please!
Doc	I sense a little tension. You seem a little uneasy.
Lorenzo	No shit.
Doc	That's not unusual for a man in your position. I've seen this a hundred times before. Let me tell you a story, Mr. Lorenzo.
Lorenzo	Can it wait?
Doc	Yes. Yes, I believe it can. (*He looks away.*) Can I ask you a personal question, Mr. Lorenzo?
Lorenzo	Shoot.
Doc	Do you love your wife?
Lorenzo	What? I... I mean... I can't...
Doc	Just answer the question please.
Lorenzo	Yes. I'm... I'm very... extremely... fond of my wife. (Doc *takes a notebook out of his pocket and writes in it.*)
Lorenzo	What the hell has that got to do with anything?
Doc	It's important to establish all the facts in a situation like this.
Lorenzo	I realise that, but I don't see...
Doc	Now I'm going to keep talking in the vain hope that you're going to shut up and listen. (*Beat.*) Thank you.

Doc *whips off the sheet that has been covering the mysterious package to reveal a toaster in a state of disrepair.* Lorenzo *gasps at the sickening sight. Pause.*

Doc	This is not a happy toaster. It's pissed off. Says you ain't been treating it right. (LORENZO *is speechless.*) Talk to me, Lorenzo.
LORENZO	Well... I don't know... what...
Doc	(*Writing in the notebook*) Sentences please, this is sounding a little like gibberish.
LORENZO	Well, how do you know?
Doc	Excuse me?
LORENZO	You seem pretty certain about your accusations.
Doc	(*Flabbergasted*) What? Are you telling me this toaster's lying?

They both stare at the toaster awaiting a response.

LORENZO	What if that's a load of cockamamie?
Doc	(*With a self-assured smile*) I've been in this game a long time, Lorenzo. I can sniff out cockamamie at a hundred paces, you slimy maggot.
LORENZO	There's no need to get...
Doc	Personal? Oh, I think there is. Maybe you don't understand the enormity of your predicament. These are serious allegations. This is almost enough to bust your ass!
LORENZO	This is ridiculous! You come into my home and treat me like a common...
Doc	Criminal! That's right. Have you understood a word I've said to you?
LORENZO	(*Pleading*) Come on. She broke down this morning; I took the afternoon off work...
Doc	So you could fix her up before your wife comes home, is that it?
LORENZO	NO! I...
Doc	RIGHT? (*No reply.*) Does she even know?
LORENZO	I didn't want to upset her or the kids.
Doc	Kids? (*Writing in notebook*) This gets better.
LORENZO	(*Exploding*) I. JUST. WANTED. TOAST. (LORENZO *slumps in the chair.*)
Doc	You are a deceitful man. (*Beat.*)

	Tell me, Lorenzo, what do you do?
LORENZO	I'm a police officer.
DOC	(*Writing*) A man of the law. Are you ashamed?
LORENZO	(*Whiny*) Yes.
DOC	(*With sudden evangelical fervour*) Now, I can fix this baby, but it's going to take a lotta time and it's gonna cost you.
LORENZO	Just name your price.
DOC	Put your money away; I don't mean greens! I mean it's gonna cost a lotta love, a whole lotta love! Are you with me?
LORENZO	Mmm…
DOC	ARE YOU WITH ME?
LORENZO	Yeah… I guess.
DOC	Are you a passionate man, Lorenzo?
LORENZO	(*Cagey*) Sometimes.
DOC	(*Writing*) This is not looking good. No, no, no. I hope to God you're a praying man 'cause it's gonna take a lot more than a screwdriver to fix this little sucker.
LORENZO	(*Welling up*) Whatever it takes. Please, fix my toaster.
DOC	Take this. (*He offers* LORENZO *a handkerchief.*) I hate to see a grown man cry. (DOC *puts on surgical gloves.*) Okay, let's get this baby up on the slab and open her up.

He removes the outer shell of the toaster so that the wires and innards are visible. LORENZO *wretches at the sight like a mutilated body.*

LORENZO	(*Making excuses to leave*) Why don't I make us some coffee?
DOC	(*Working on the toaster like a surgeon*) No thanks, I don't take coffee when I'm on duty: gives me the shakes.
LORENZO	Well, if you're sure. (*Leaving*) I'm just gonna…
DOC	Wait! Is this a hard water area?
LORENZO	(*Stops*) I dunno… I think so.

Doc	Do you have a limescale filter?
Lorenzo	No.
Doc	(*Getting the notebook*) How often do you de-scale the filament?
Lorenzo	I dunno... once, twice a month.

Doc *drops the notebook on the table: he is devastated, close to tears. He takes the hanky from* Lorenzo *and begins to wipe his eyes.*

Doc	That breaks my heart. (*He begins to put the toaster back together.*) You people have no idea. You just don't get it, do you? Do you have any notion of what limescale can do to a kettle? (Lorenzo *doesn't reply. There is fear in his eyes.*) You ever heard of cholesterol?
Lorenzo	Sure.
Doc	(*Mocking*) Sure! 'Course you have, 'cause cholesterol affects you, right? (*Pointing to the ceiling*) What kind of wattage you got in those bulbs there?
Lorenzo	(*Guessing*) Sixty? Hundred watt?
Doc	You've got a desk lamp in your study, I saw it on my way in. What wattage is that?
Lorenzo	(*Bluffing*) Sixty.
Doc	Sixty? Yeah? What kind of fuse have you got?
Lorenzo	Er... well, I...
Doc	(*Impatient*) What voltage?
Lorenzo	(*Also losing patience*) I dunno... thirteen.
Doc	Thirteen? (*Feigning amusement*) You're telling me you've got a thirteen amp fuse for sixty watt bulb? (*Laughs*) (Lorenzo *goes along with the joke.*) Are you joking? Is that it? (*Getting nasty*) Are you taking me for a fool? Are you toying with me, Lorenzo? Don't toy with me!
Lorenzo	I don't know what voltage it is. I don't buy the fuses. My wife does!
Doc	Oh, your wife buys them. You are not fit to own an electrical appliance! YOU ARE INHUMANE!

> (*He takes a pet carry-case from under the table and puts the toaster inside. Calmly*) I've got all the evidence I need (*proffering notebook*) to put your ass behind bars for a bitch of a long time. You will never see your toaster again. EVER!

DOC *starts to leave but* LORENZO *grabs a screwdriver from* DOC's *breast pocket and threatens him with it.*

LORENZO   (*Running on adrenaline*) You ain't going nowhere! Now you get your self-righteous ass back there and fix my toaster!

They square up to each other, face to face. The tension is growing by the second which is visible on LORENZO's *flushed, twitchy face.* DOC, *however, remains remarkably calm and stolid, almost arrogant in his grip on the situation.*

DOC   (*After a long drawn out pause*) You're not really gonna use that thing are you?

LORENZO   You bet I'm gonna fucking use it!

DOC   You really shouldn't point one of those things if you're not prepared to use it.

LORENZO   (*Bluffing*) I ain't bluffing.

DOC   I never said you were, Mr. Toughguy. (*Drawn out*) I just don't think you've got the balls.

LORENZO   (*Panicky*) Don't fuck with me!

DOC   I ain't fucking with anybody. I reckon you're chicken shit.

LORENZO   You know, you're pretty cocky for a guy who's about to be impaled by a Phillips screwdriver.
(*Pause. The tension builds.*)

DOC   That ain't a Phillips.
(*Pause. Unblinking eye contact.*)

LORENZO   What?

DOC   It's a flat head.

Huge pause as sweat pours down LORENZO's *face. He glances down to see if what* DOC *said is true. As* LORENZO *looks down,* DOC *seizes his opportunity to take control and grabs the screwdriver. As he lunges, however,* LORENZO *pulls back out of the way and assumes his original threat position.*

LORENZO	Don't try it! Don't even think about trying anything funny!
DOC	(*Losing composure for a short but vital moment*) Okay, but I don't think you're in a position to tell me what to do.
LORENZO	Oh, I think I am. I'm pointing a screwdriver at your chest. Can you think of a better reason?
DOC	One. Let's just say you make one false move and toasty gets it.
	(DOC *stretches out the carry-case as if to drop it.*)
LORENZO	You wouldn't dare.
DOC	Wouldn't I? (*He wobbles the basket a little.*)
LORENZO	Okay, okay!
DOC	Think about it.
LORENZO	What's to say you ain't bluffing.
DOC	Try me.
LORENZO	Okay, you win. Please don't hurt my baby.

LORENZO *puts the screwdriver down on the table and backs away.* DOC *throws* LORENZO *the hanky to wipe his eyes and then picks up the screwdriver with his free hand.*

DOC	Now I've got both. Ha! (LORENZO *looks miffed wiping his eyes.*) First rule in a hostage situation, didn't they teach you that at school?
	(DOC *backs* LORENZO *into the chair and puts the carry-case on the table.*)
LORENZO	I don't know what the hell kind of school you went to, but it sure the hell wasn't mine. (*Pleading*) Please, Mr. Doc, fix my toaster. If you have any compassion, please fix my toaster.
DOC	(*Manic screeching. We are now peeking under the lid of*

the boiling innards of a deeply troubled mind.)
Compassion? COMPASSION! (*Disguising his
outburst with formality. Deadpan.*) Are you a
compassionate man, Mr. Lorenzo?

Lorenzo   Well…

Doc   Don't answer that! You people have got a lot to
learn about compassion. (*Choking up*) Do you even
know what a crumb tray is? Or a rusty heating
element? Or a damaged casing? Or poor
ventilation? Overheating or a faulty plug? Do you
know much damage granary bread can do? DO
YOU? (Lorenzo *hangs his head in shame.*) I think it's
time for that story now.

Lorenzo *welcomes the change of subject and nods, relieved.* Doc
shoots him a stony look and he melts into the chair. Doc *takes his time,
wrestling with some inner demon, like a psychiatrist who has pressed
all the right buttons.* Lorenzo *looks on powerless against the torrent.
It's all coming out now and* Lorenzo *is in the blast zone.*

Doc   (*Struggling*) I was only eleven. I was just a kid. Our
toaster broke down one day just before breakfast. I
remember it well because my dad left for work on
an empty stomach; that always made him mad. He
left me in charge. I told him I could fix it; he trusted
me. It was my responsibility, I was the oldest, oldest
of fifteen brothers. We didn't see dad much; he
seemed to care more about his church than he did
about us. This was my one chance to prove
myself… (*choking up*) to make him notice.
          (*He begins to reenact the story with the toaster in
          front of him.*)
          I didn't know what the hell I was doing. I took the
          top off her just to have a look around. I'd… I'd
          never seen the inside of a toaster before. I didn't
          know what was wrong. I was just poking around
          blindly and all the time she was dying right in front
          of me. I knew I hadn't got much time but I tried

everything. I must've changed every single one of those components, but nothing worked. In the end, I had to leave her. She died right there in my arms. I'll never forget that.

(A single tear rolls down his cheek. LORENZO *offers* DOC *the handkerchief, waving it in the air by way of a peace offering and a surrender.* DOC *takes the hanky and finishes the story.)*

I rushed straight home from school that day before dad got back. I had a flash of inspiration; there was one place I still hadn't checked. I opened up the *plug... (He unscrews the plug of the real toaster.)* ... And there it was... the fuse had blown. *(He holds the fuse up for* LORENZO's *inspection.)* The poor little thing had had a heart attack. So I changed the fuse as quickly as I could, but she was never the same.

(He produces a new fuse from his pocket and repairs the toaster.)

I knew that and my father knew that. He never looked me in the eye after that. I failed him... and I failed my toaster. I never did that again. So what's your story, Lorenzo?

*(*LORENZO *is so overcome with emotion that he can't speak: he just shrugs.* DOC *throws him the hanky and finishes his work in silence.)*

There. Should be okay now. Sure, it's never gonna be the same, but it'll toast your bread.

DOC *gets two slices of bread from his pockets, puts them in the toaster and pushes down the button. He gathers his instruments and the carry-case.*

LORENZO	So that's it?
DOC	Yeah.
LORENZO	I just wanna thank...
DOC	Don't. I do what I have to.

Doc *picks up a motorcycle helmet that has been concealed under the table.* Lorenzo *gives him the hanky.*

Doc   Keep it. You might need it.

He puts on the helmet and gives a casual salute. He snaps down the visor of the helmet and swaggers out the door to find a sunset to ride into.

Lorenzo *turns to the audience clutching the sacred hanky. He is physically and emotionally exhausted, but there is a serene quality to his worldly-wise smile.*

There is a short pause as the audience clocks Lorenzo's *haggard demeanour. The toast pops up, preferably with a big, charcoal smiling face on it. This is possible… thanks to the miracles of technology. Quick fade to black.*

COLM BERRILL

Chair

Colm Berrill was born in Ireland. Before joining the writing course at UEA, he studied English at De Montfort University. He is working on his first novel.

Mattie Kenelly sat and stared. Mattie never did anything else. That morning, as was usual, his mother had lifted him from his bed, washed him, dressed him, fed him, and placed him in his designated chair in the sitting-room. His positioning allowed him an unrestricted view of the many and varied events which might take place on the street outside, but all of this was of no consequence to Mattie. Mattie was batty. He had not however, always been batty. It was five years, nine months and eleven days since everything had stopped making sense to Mattie. Five years, nine months and eleven days since Mattie had exhibited any propensity to motion. Every bodily function which did not occur spontaneously and of its own accord was initiated by his mother with the occasional begrudging assistance of his sister. Beneath a pair of his father's trousers, conveniently two sizes too big for him, he wore an arrangement of absorbent nappies, towelling and plastic pants into which he would shit and piss at frequent and unpredictable intervals with no discernible indication of either effort or discomfort.

It had all begun with a chair. Not a chair bearing any resemblance to the one on which he now sat but a wooden, four-legged, straight-backed, rather plain, but eminently functional, dining chair. Sometime longer than five years, nine months and eleven days ago, the very chair which now rested quite inconspicuously by the table in the dining room had begun to cause some concern to Mattie. The chair had not done anything, nothing beyond being a chair and being in a position to be sat upon, but, nonetheless, Mattie had started to think about it and think about it and think about it and think about it and think about it until he couldn't get it out of his head. Although at first his ruminations on the chair had been relatively nebulous in form, they had gradually become fixed on one particular aspect of its existence. Specifically, what Mattie couldn't work out was, why the chair was a chair. He couldn't puzzle out the relationship between this word, chair, and the object which resided in the dining-room of Kenelly's boarding-house. In his mind he was unable to form any connection between the two and eventually they ceased to connect at all. Mattie found himself repeating 'chair' over and over in his head but was now totally incapable of conjuring up any image of the object to which the word related. He had never been particularly bright, but he was a strapping lad with a pleasant nature and not afraid of hard work and, with the aid of a bottle of whiskey and a significant donation to the Parish Priest's housekeeping fund, Mrs Kenelly had secured his engagement as a casual gravedigger at Mountpleasant Cemetery. Mattie enjoyed his work immensely but so serious was his concern regarding this particular chair that one day, he simply dropped his spade into the shallow hole of an unfinished grave and set off for home. He proceeded directly to the dining-room, removed the offending article from its place and, lifting it above his head, began a thorough examination of its form and construction. He scrutinised its legs, back, seat and all the supporting joints and still he could see no connection between the word and the object. His mother, naturally concerned to see him home at such an unexpected hour of the day and surprised by the absence of any greeting or explanation for his premature return from the cemetery, followed him into the dining-room.

"Mattie, what's the matter? What're you doing home at this time?"

"Chair," said Mattie.

"What?"

"Chair."

"What're you going on about, Mattie? What're you doing home?"

"Chair."

"What're you talking about, Mattie? I know it's a chair. What's wrong with it?"

"Chair," said Mattie.

"Will ye put the feckin chair down, ye feckin eejit?"

Mrs Kenelly was somewhat irate by now and reaching up, grabbed the chair off Mattie and banged it down on the floor. She stared at Mattie.

"Chair," said he, pointing at the object.

"Mattie, will ye for God's sake tell me what the feck ye're going on about?"

"Chair."

It seemed to have totally escaped Mattie's attention that there were in fact, another eleven chairs, all bearing a remarkable resemblance to the chair in question, placed at regular intervals around the dining-room table, but they were of no import to Mattie. He picked up the chair and carried it to the sitting-room. There, he placed it in front of the window and, seating himself nearby, began his contemplation of 'chair'.

At this point, Mrs Kenelly, totally flummoxed, ran to fetch the Widow Kenelly. Sisters by marriage, Mrs Kenelly had had the misfortune to marry the widow's late husband's brother, a commercial traveller in animal feeds who, some years previously, had taken off with a farmer's daughter from Carrick-on-Shannon. Somewhat warily, the Widow entered the sitting-room and approached Mattie.

"Mattie love," said she, "What's de matter, Mattie?"

"Chair," said Mattie.

"Mattie, sure haven't choo gotchore mother in an awful state now? What on earth can de matter be?"

"Chair," said he.

"He's not right Mary", said she turning to Mrs Kenelly. "I tink y'id better get de doctor in."

There followed some debate on this matter concluding with the decision that it might be better to call for the nuns first. Within the hour, Sister Monica of the Holy Order of Merciful Mothers of God was on the doorstep. Ushered in to the sitting-room, Sister Monica made the mistake of sitting on the chair. Mattie's right arm shot out and, gesticulating furiously at some undefined point between the nun's legs, yelled at the top of his voice, "Chair, chair, chair, chair, chair, chair...", stopping only when the nun, not in the habit of being addressed in this most undignified of manners and with an indecency of haste known only to those in the righteous service of their god, leapt from the chair and seizing both Mrs Kenelly and the Widow by the arms retreated to the dining-room.

"He's definitely not right," she affirmed. "This would be a matter for Father Mulcahy."

On reciting five decades of the rosary and finally being persuaded to accept five pounds for her trouble, Sister Monica departed.

The Parish Priest, Father Mulcahy, met with a similar response and, having anointed Mattie with holy water and offering numerous devotions for the healing of the afflicted, finally accepted ten pounds for his strenuous efforts and suggested that, whilst it was highly unlikely anything could be done in such matters of the spirit, it might be worth consulting a member of the medical profession on Mattie's condition.

So it was then that Mrs Kenelly placed Mattie under the care of Doctor Shine, Chief Consultant in Affairs of the Spirit at St. Patrick's Institute for the Emotionally Distressed. Despite many months of intensive therapy, Mattie's condition worsened. Whilst he no longer craved the presence of the chair, he also no longer spoke. Not even to say 'chair'. He did not move and would not eat or drink of his own volition. Having been persuaded to accept seventeen hundred and fifty-six pounds for his undoubted troubles, Doctor Shine eventually concluded that it would be best for Mattie to return home. Mrs Kenelly took it upon herself, with the assistance of Mattie's younger sister Eileen, her only other offspring, to care for him as best they could in the relative comfort of the Kenelly boarding house.

Mattie's existence revolved around consumption and expulsion. Both were problematic. Feeding him by traditional means had eventually proved too time-consuming for Mrs Kenelly. He would neither chew food nor swallow liquid without the intervention of another party. This necessitated the manual manipulation of his jaws until each mouthful of food had achieved the necessary consistency and then tilting his head back at a sharp angle until a quantity of liquid could be presented which would expedite its progression to his stomach.

Needless to say, with the responsibilities of running the house and of attending to its guests weighing heavily upon her, Mrs Kenelly was forced to devise some other, more efficient way of feeding Mattie. After some considerable thought she developed a system which seemed to satisfy the needs of all concerned. Having first pureed the ingredients and placed the resulting mixture in a deep jug, Mrs Kenelly would, rather in the method of a siphoning system, suck the liquid into a long plastic tube. Having lubricated the end of the tube she would then slide it down Mattie's throat until it entered his stomach. To some extent the food would then proceed of its own accord from jug to stomach. As was often the case however, the presence in excess of lard and other indefinable masses in Mrs Kenelly's cooking, would slow or prevent the smooth progress of the victuals and at this point Mrs Kenelly would blow quite forcibly down the other end of the tube clearing any blockages and so ensure its safe passage into Mattie. At no point did Mattie ever show any sign of pleasure or displeasure either at the method of his feeding or the nature of his food. The expulsion of the comestibles was a much less involved procedure for Mattie. He simply shat and pissed at will. For Mrs Kenelly, however – Eileen would have no part in this – it was a much messier operation. Mattie seemed to produce quantities of liquid excrement which seemed proportionally impossible in relation to the quantities he consumed. Nevertheless, it was a task which had to be performed and despite the qualities of absorption claimed by various manufacturers of adult disposable nappies, there was always a faecal coating of concrete consistency to be scraped and scrubbed from Mattie's arse and general genital area. Its odour was certainly unique and pervaded every room of the house.

Had it not been for the arrival of Frankie Devaney, it can only be assumed that the day-to-day pattern of Mattie's life would have remained unaltered until either he or his mother died. As things turned out however, that was not to be the case. Being a young man fresh from the country and new to the ways of the city and city people, Frankie was at first quite shy, even reticent, in his dealings with both the Kenellys and the other residents of the house. As he found his feet though, he realised that each could offer new and exciting forms of distraction. Mattie would always be stationed in the sitting-room of the house from before the guests would have their breakfast until after they had retired to their rooms. Mrs Kenelly found it preferable to have the room to herself while ministering to her son's needs. It was customary for the guests, after the evening meal, to spend a couple of hours in the sitting-room. It was a ritual entirely of Mrs Kenelly's contrivance and existed only to afford her the opportunity to interrogate her residents politely on the progress of their various employments and assure herself of their ability to pay the rent. Mattie of course, was present at all of these gatherings, being unable to remove himself from the room and Mrs Kenelly being of the opinion that the company of others could only be beneficial to his condition. Inevitably, the subject of Mattie would arise in some of these conversations and by dribs and drabs Frankie eventually familiarised himself with the full circumstances of Mattie's plight.

At first Frankie simply sought to spend time alone with Mattie. He would sit and observe him. At times even attempt to engage him in conversation, all of course to no avail. Mrs Kenelly was delighted that a young man like Frankie should demonstrate such compassion for the spiritually tormented and was more than happy to allow him to spend as much time as possible with Mattie, even to the extent of shooing the other residents off to their rooms at an unnaturally early hour. Frankie welcomed this alteration in the balance of the Kenelly household. As time went by, he was further encouraged to spend more time with Mattie and even allowed to assist Mrs Kenelly and Eileen in the ritual of feeding. Frankie could see an unlimited number of possibilities opening up before him, all of which would satisfy his craving for distraction.

His interference with Mattie took a relatively limited form to begin with. He was well aware of the extent to which Mrs Kenelly yearned for some sign of improvement in Mattie and endeavoured to offer her some indication that a change might be in the air. One night, while Mrs Kenelly was busy in the kitchen and he and Mattie were alone, Frankie crossed Mattie's right leg over his left leg. Then, saying goodnight to Mrs Kenelly, he adjourned to his bedroom. The next morning Mrs Kenelly was full of it. She couldn't believe it. Mattie had moved! It was a miracle! The hand of God was in the house!

Galvanised by the effect of his opening move Frankie determined to continue in his manoeuvrings of Mattie. Two nights later he not only crossed Mattie's legs (left over right this time – simply for variation) but folded his arms as well. The outcome was spectacular. Mrs Kenelly was in raptures. She began offering novenas to Saint Anthony, prayers to Our Blessed Lady of Dolours, Saint Joseph and all the Apostles. Even the quantity of food provided for her guests increased.

Whilst this was all very entertaining to Frankie, somehow he felt that there must be something more he could do. One of the greatest pleasures in becoming more involved with Mattie was that it had furnished him with the opportunity to observe Eileen Kenelly at closer quarters. Whenever her mother was too busy to tend to Mattie, Eileen would assume responsibility for his nutritional well-being. Frankie would sit in an armchair, watching, waiting, praying for the feeding tube to block. Eileen was a buxom girl with a propensity to tight blouses and Frankie derived intense pleasure from the sight of her inhaling deeply, filling her lungs, and expanding her wonderful chest before taking the plastic tube between her sensuous lips and blowing pureed semolina as hard as she could into Mattie's gullet. On occasion Frankie would suggest that it might be helpful if he held Mattie's shoulders from behind while she blew and this presented him, if the blouse was suitably cut, with an exquisite glimpse of her heaving cleavage. He began to wonder if there wasn't some way in which he could combine his penchant for distraction and his distraction with Eileen to some greater, more satisfactory purpose.

Keeping that thought in mind, he decided to be a little more adventurous in his doings with Mattie. He'd been crossing and uncrossing legs and folding and unfolding arms and tilting and untilting heads and clenching and unclenching fists and closing and opening eyes for several weeks now, but was finding that, whilst each new development was initially greeted with ecstasy by Mrs Kenelly, eventually the shine would wear off and things would revert to their familiar state of mundanity.

The tea did not work as well as Frankie had anticipated. Having gone to the trouble of sneaking down to the kitchen in the middle of the night, risking all manner of repercussions had he been caught, and placing a half-drunk cup of tea on the locker by Mattie's bed, Frankie was utterly dismayed when no mention was made of the incident. He could only conclude that Mrs Kenelly assumed that she herself had left the tea there when putting Mattie to bed. This called for something more drastic. Still persisting with his manipulations of as many of Mattie's limbs and organs as he feasibly could, Frankie waited a week and then, on the pretext of needing some fresh air (an understandable requirement given Mattie's tendency to random evacuations), Frankie left the house. A short time later he returned and went directly to his room. Concealed about his person were two saveloys, one fishcake, and a large portion of chips with salt and vinegar. After consuming more than half of his purchases Frankie sat and waited. When a suitable interval had passed and the house was quiet he entered Mattie's room where he deposited the bulk of the remaining food on the bedside locker. He rubbed a couple of chips and half a saveloy vigorously around Mattie's mouth and then dropped them down the front of Mattie's striped pyjama top.

The pandemonium which ensued the following morning was beyond Frankie's wildest imaginings. The residents were woken by a veritable torrent of expletives as Mrs Kenelly exploded at Mattie. She dragged his limp and utterly unresponsive body from the bed and slapping him by turn on both the left and right sides of his face decried him as a fraud.

Slap!

"Ye durty feckin wee shite! Have me for a feckin fool, woodje? Ye bastard. Ye're no feckin son of mine."

Slap!

"Ye lyin little fucker. I'll have ye're fuckin guts fer garters."

Slap!

And so on, until Eileen eventually dragged her from Mattie's flaccid frame and calmed her enough to point out that whatever he may have been up to during the night, he certainly wasn't responding now. Frankie was delighted. Now he felt truly at liberty to advance with the next stage of his plan.

There was one other resident of the house for whom Frankie had cultivated a particular dislike. Maurice Donoghue was one of the longest standing of Mrs Kenelly's guests. A junior clerk in a firm of conveyancers and the son of an assistant undermanager in the Ballyratoath branch of the Bank of Leinster, he had certain notions of superiority which were a constant source of irritation to Frankie. Donoghue also had ideas of getting into Eileen Kenelly's knickers. Now Frankie had already been in Eileen's knickers. Unfortunately for him though, not while she was wearing them. Eileen had just completed her secondary education but had long since completed her sexual education and in accordance with that, as Frankie discovered, had a chest of drawers containing a diversity of underwear sufficient to stock a small, but undoubtedly popular, chain of lingerie shops. Whenever the opportunity arose, Frankie would avail himself of some appealing item from this chest and after an extended period of masturbation, ejaculate copiously into it before returning it to the drawer. Whether Eileen was aware of this, Frankie neither knew nor cared.

As soon as he reasonably could, Frankie acquired from Eileen's drawers, seven pairs of panties (of varying colours, design and material, but including white satin, red nylon triloball, and a particularly fine pair in black polyester trimmed with lace), one pair of mauve knickers in the French style, one basque, three brassieres (two black, one flesh-tone), and four pairs of stockings. He was well aware that Eileen could not fail to notice the absence of these items and that speed of execution was paramount if his plan was to succeed. That evening during Mrs Kenelly's post-dinner interrogation, Frankie excused himself and went to his room. Keeping aside only two pairs of panties (white satin and black polyester), Frankie took the rest of the underwear and secreted it at the bottom of Maurice Donoghue's wardrobe. Returning to the sitting-room Frankie stayed until everyone else had left for bed and even helped Mrs Kenelly feed Mattie. Later, in his room, Frankie sat on the edge

of his bed playing with his cock. Wrapped around the glans was
the pair of white satin panties. Once his enjoyment was complete
and the panties were liberally coated, Frankie made his way to
Mattie's room. He pulled back Mattie's bedclothes and, undoing
his pyjamas, wrapped the panties around Mattie's penis. As a
finishing touch, Frankie took Mattie's right hand and, with
perhaps an unnecessary degree of precision, moulded it round
the pantie-encased penis. This task accomplished, Frankie
returned to his room and, with a contented smile, relaxed and
awaited the following morning's developments. Certain they
wouldn't be missed, he kept the black polyester knickers
for himself.

Emma Brooker

from *The Deal*

Emma Brooker worked as a journalist before studying at UEA. She lives in London. *The Deal* is her first novel.

It was late July, a wasps and melted ice-cream day full of trippers dithering around in kid-packed cars trying to find the coast. Jeff was in a bad mood, I was map-reading and we were lost. I couldn't think of a worse combination.

We were trying to find the farm which had advertised 'young couple wanted for work and accommodation' in the local paper. The phone number they gave didn't work so we'd decided to look for the place – Bethlem Farm – we knew it was somewhere in the stretch of fens north of town. We'd both gone through the area loads of times on the way to the beach, but once we came off the main road we were as lost as the rest, surrounded by big fields, big sky and long roads which went straight ahead for miles and ended up nowhere.

"We need to ask the way," I said and picked a line on the map with a cluster of dots at the end of it. We set off hopefully in that direction, but what had looked like a village on paper turned out to be two houses, a line of washing and a brick pumping station next to a gurgling dyke. A combine harvester inched noiselessly across the horizon, but there was nobody in sight. Nobody to ask. The only way out was to turn back.

"We're nearly out of petrol," said Jeff. It was the second time we'd reached a dead end. His teeth seemed to be locked together.

"I'm sure it's over that way." I waved towards a cropstore in the distance which I hadn't noticed before. Jeff turned the car around and drove until we reached a level crossing and had to sit and wait as a train lilted past. A fly buzzed in through the window.

"I wish we'd never done this," said Jeff. He was gripping the steering wheel so hard his knuckles stuck out. I remember how sharp and white they looked.

"We?" I was going to point out that he was the one who lost

his job for nicking stuff and couldn't keep up with the rent. But it didn't seem worth it.

"It'll be all right," I said and when I heard myself I realised that I meant it. On days like that, with a soaring blue sky and the heat soaked right through to your bones, it's hard to believe that things won't work out. One way or another.

When the train passed and the barrier finally went up, Jeff stepped on the accelerator and we spun down the empty road so fast I had to yell stop when I saw the sign. Bethlem Farm. It was done in fresh paint with drips on old board and planted in the verge next to a turning. We jerked forward and back as he slammed the brakes, and looked at each other for a second. Jeff crunched the gears, reversed and took the turning.

It was a private road, pitted with potholes which made the car scrape and roll. The field to our right was planted with baby cabbages, in rows which made me think of a lost army buried up to the neck in dark brown earth. To the left was a crop of rape with the seed set and most of the yellow flowers gone. The afternoon sun threw long shadows across the fields and the shape of the car loomed ahead of us.

At first I couldn't see the house. It was about quarter of a mile from the main road and was concealed by a screen of conifers planted to form a high hedge, like a lot of the farms round there. The bad road and the weeds growing thick in the fields did not promise much.

"I bet they pay shit money," said Jeff as though it was my fault. His chin stuck out in anger.

The road followed a bend and we turned into the drive leading up to the first of two houses. Someone was standing at the window, waiting for us. They must have heard the car or seen the plume of dust which followed us there.

Jeff pulled up and switched the engine off. Some dogs barked angrily inside the house and there was a slight thudding as they jumped up inside the front door. I could see now it was a woman standing at the window. She was pointing, telling us to go to the back door, and when we got there she was standing on the step, smiling. A tall woman in her late thirties, early forties, hard to say, wearing a black and red kimono-style dressing gown.

"You saw the ad?" She had a deep voice and a sleepy look. "I've been sunbathing," she said gesturing down at her clothes. "Got to make the most of this weather." There was a beach smell of coconut around her, a smear of oil on her chin and her black hair was piled up on top of her head with a big clip making her tall. Maybe it was the lipstick and eye shadow she was wearing but she instantly came across as stylish, even though she wasn't dressed properly. I suddenly felt uncomfortably scruffy in the shorts and T shirt I'd chucked on that morning.

She looked at us, narrowed her eyes for a second and then said, "Would you like some squash?" and smiled. It was as though she'd been hoping for a visitors all afternoon and realised she'd better make the most of us. Jeff and I, still standing on the doorstep, nodded.

"Well, come in then!" She moved back into the cool of the kitchen and as Jeff stepped forward onto the pristine lino an Alsation leapt out of the shadows behind her and bounded towards us, barking. I shrank back.

"Rufus," she shouted and grabbed him by his collar. "Bad boy." She ruffled his ears affectionately. "Now make friends." The dog stared at us, nothing moving except the wet of his sniffing nose.

"Go on Rufus, make friends with the new people." She smiled at us again. "I'm Margaret by the way."

The dog's mouth dropped open, and his pink tongue lolled out on one side. He panted and whimpered, looking to her, then back to us.

"Don't mind us doggy," muttered Jeff and seeing that it had scared us, it lost interest, yawned and trotted to the other side of the room, claws clicking on the lino. We went in to a large airy kitchen, immaculately clean and free from the sticky heat of the day. It had windows looking out in two directions across the expansive fields.

"Orange squash?" asked Margaret, flip flopping over to the sink as Jeff and I sat down at the red Formica-topped table. The ties of her dressing gown fluttered loose. She was wearing a swimming costume underneath and she had plastic flowers on her shoes.

"Security's a problem round here. That's why the dogs are so jumpy," she said, toying with the gold chain around her neck. Her accent was neutral. I couldn't tell if she was local or not.

Some bracelets jangled along her arm as she reached to open a cupboard and took out two tall glasses and a matching jug which she filled with squash and ice and put down in front of us. The drink had a chemical smell and made my mouth feel dry. I sucked on an ice cube.

"Do you come from round here or are you just passing through?"

"We're living in town at the moment." Luckily Jeff seemed to have cheered up – at least he was on best behaviour. "But we've both done farm work before. We were working in the south this last Spring cutting flowers and then some soft fruit but we..." he trailed off.

In the car we'd agreed not to mention the supermarket which fired Jeff but where I still worked.

"Got tired of moving around all the time," I added. "And living out of the back of the car."

"Some of them give you a mobile home," Jeff chipped in.

"But then you're sharing with six other people," I said.

Margaret screwed her nose up in distaste. She saw me looking at a plate of biscuits with white lumps in them she had put out. "Chocolate, would you like one?" She pushed the plate towards me. I took one and put it on the red table in front of me, next to my glass.

I still couldn't guess her age. Her mouth had something slack, almost elastic about it, but her eyes were bright and tight. She had quite bony hands with orange-red nails and a big emerald ring on her wedding finger.

"Yes. Security. We're looking for a couple to help on the farm and move into the cottage over there. It's been empty for ages, but it's got all the essentials. Sky View. It's a sweet little place really."

Jeff and I twisted round in our chairs to look through the door at the modern red brick house she was pointing at further down the track. The uncurtained windows looked dark and unwelcoming.

"Someone stole a lot of machinery from the shed down there last year," she went on. "They must have taken ages, loading it all into a van, but the dogs were shut in and the nearest neighbours are about half a mile away and you can't ask them to keep a constant watch on the place. I mean, we'd spend our whole time spying on each other wouldn't we?" She laughed, throwing her head back, and I saw her fillings.

"The quiet can drive you mad sometimes," she said nodding out of the window at the fields. "Specially if you're a townie like me. But I do like the privacy. You don't have to bother drawing your curtains round here."

Jeff shifted in his chair. A breeze rattled one of the windows and the bright sunlight faltered through a scudding cloud. I bit into my biscuit and put it back on the table. It wasn't chocolate, it was almond and it tasted like classroom glue.

"We had another scare recently, so we let some of the dogs run loose now when we go out. I breed them you see. Rufus has fathered most of the Alsations you meet round here, but that's not enough. We decided we had to get people living in that house."

"Are we the first..." Jeff asked, but the phone rang and Margaret went into the hall to answer it.

"Yes darling they're here." I could see Margaret through the open door, perched on a chair with the dog curled up at her feet. "They seem perfectly fine, perfect, very young," she said quite loudly, as though we couldn't hear.

"Seems all right, doesn't it?" Jeff mumbled in my direction.

"I don't know," I whispered. I was beginning to realise how few options we really had. Jeff took my hand under the table and held it between both of his which was his way of saying sorry for being bad tempered.

Suddenly Margaret was back standing over the table, telling us to drink up, like a bossy mum. "Peter – my husband – he saw you arrive and said to send you over to look at the cottage." The dog had come with her and I felt its wagging tail knocking against my leg.

"You haven't asked about us yet," Jeff smiled nervously. "Is there anything else you need to know?"

"Why, are you hiding something from me Jeffrey?" she chuckled ruffling his hair as though he was a little kid and making him blush.

"Don't worry dear," she said breezily, "It's the usual deal – the house is rent free and you get paid once a fortnight for the farm work. Anyway, off you go. Peter's on his way over. He'll go through the details with you." She took a bunch of keys from a hook behind the door, pressed it into Jeff's hand and bustled us out. "See you later I hope." The door clunked shut and suddenly we were back in the bright sun.

"I suppose we might as well go and have a look at it?" Jeff held the keys in the palm of his hand as though he was trying to guess their weight. He was asking me to make a decision either way, and I don't know why but I wanted to say, let's give the keys back and go. Just drive away back to town and borrow some money to pay the rent until you find another job. But then I thought of the squash and biscuits and the husband coming over to meet us. What would we say if we met him on the road? It would seem rude and hard to explain, so I said, "OK. We might as well. It's not far."

The cottage, built on a square of land taken from the edge of a vast field looked like a child's drawing, a floating shape, with nothing around it to give a sense of size or distance. When we started walking towards it looked like a small building that was nearby, but the further we got down the track, the bigger and further away it turned out to be. What looked like a short walk took more than five minutes.

The track leading there was in bad condition, with deep tyre grooves made in wet weather and hardened like cement in the heat. Half way along I turned back and saw Margaret framed in the glass of the back door. A small shape now, she was watching us and she waved.

I was hungry and I thought of the peaches and the ice cream and pre-roasted chicken and profiteroles we'd enjoyed a few nights ago. It was typical of Jeff's bad luck getting caught on the supermarket security video stuffing all that food up the front of his jacket. They'd decided to run through the footage just to check that the camera worked.

"They could still press charges you know." Jeff had been thinking about the same thing.

"They won't do that."

Sky View was surrounded by a rickety fence which had brambles and nettles growing through it. The gate was missing and a section of fence lay flat on the ground with some old fertiliser sacks and rusty tins thrown on top of it. Whatever that fence was first intended to keep in or out had been and gone. What was left looked like a crumpled gesture of defiance against the vast flat fields stretching into the distance all around.

"Adder country," said Jeff brandishing a flimsy stick he had found on the track. As we walked up the path to the chalky blue front, the lock caught the light and sparkled. I took Jeff's hand and unfolded his fingers.

"Look. New lock and key." It must have been changed that morning or the day before because there were still some wood shavings on the step.

Jeff turned the key, pushed open the door and we walked into the hall. The air inside was stiff with summer heat and a rancid smell of mouldy clothes, stale smoke and fried food.

"What a stink." Jeff held his nose and carried on talking. "Still, it's better than it looks from the outside."

Through the door on the right was the lounge, full of orange light. I pulled the curtains open and we both looked around at the furniture – a big settee and coffee table with a pub ashtray in the middle of it. There was a gas fire with a framed picture above it of an Alpine landscape printed on metallic-looking paper.

Jeff straightened the picture. "It's not such a dump is it?"

"Depends what you're comparing with." I shrugged and wandered into the kitchen. The floor was sticky with dirt and there was a greasy plate by the sink and a mug of old coffee or tea covered in a skin of mould. In the fridge was an old pint of milk, the end of a loaf of bread, and an unopened pack of chicken thighs. The fridge was plugged in but not working.

"Look Jeff. Someone's only just left." He poked his head round the kitchen door. "I thought she said it had been empty for years?"

"I don't know. Maybe they had some friends staying here. But I do know that the fewer questions we ask them, the less they're going to ask us." I rolled my eyes. "Think about it Liz. I'm not going to get any job where I need a reference am I?"

He turned and thumped up the stairs, two at a time and I felt the walls shake slightly. Upstairs there were two rooms which might once have been kids' bedrooms judging by the sugar pink and blue walls. They were completely empty apart from a couple of mousetraps. The bathroom was dark, with dribbling tap stains in the bath and a mould bloom on the ceiling. There was a plastic bag in the basin full of toothpaste, soap, shaving cream, lipstick. I tested the tap. The water had been switched off.

"I don't think it could have been friends of theirs. They seem to have left in a real hurry. Jeff?"

I walked into the main bedroom and Jeff jumped out at me from behind the door, pushed me onto the bed, pinned my arms down with his knees and started tickling me.

"Stop it you bastard," I screamed and tried to kick him off. The more I struggled, the more he laughed, so I went limp and played dead. That was when I saw the jacket on the back of the door. It gave me a fright, like seeing another person in the room.

"It feels like these people could come back any minute." I stood up. "They've left sheets on the bed." I opened the wardrobe and found a sports bag full of jumpers and another plastic bag with men's and women's shoes jumbled together inside. "You don't just leave stuff like this behind when you move. Do you?"

"They'll probably come back and collect it. You can ask them all about it then." Jeff was sprawled on the bed with his hands behind his head. "Come on Liz, don't spoil it," he said with a big grin. "It's nice in here."

The bedroom was certainly better than the rest of the house. A big double bed covered with a green bedspread seemed to fill the room, and the window looked out over a field full of ripening wheat. The white walls had taken the pink gold light of the afternoon sun.

"I think she liked us that woman Margaret. This is our big chance." A wheedling tone had crept into his voice. "What else are we going to do?"

A car door slammed and we both jumped as we heard a boot scrape on the door step. Jeff leapt up and straightened the bedspread. I went out onto the landing. The front door must have been left wide open because when I looked down from the top of the stairs the elongated shadow of whoever it was on the step filled the hall.

"Helloo. Anyone in there?" A man's voice called and as he stepped over the threshold he looked up and saw me. "I didn't mean to startle you. Maggie said you'd be over here." He stuck his hand out and Jeff, who had pushed past me on the stairs, reached forward and shook it.

"Cosy little place isn't it?" he said turning to me. "My grandfather had it built for my father when he was in his early twenties, before he took over the farm. I think he wanted to keep an eye on him. Keep him in his sights." Then he stopped talking and looked at me while he scratched his chin. "Don't I know you?" he smiled. His blonde fleshy features were not familiar but I supposed he could have noticed me in town and remembered my face. To say 'no' would have seemed rude, so I smiled back at him.

"It's perfect, just right for us," I heard Jeff say.

I don't know if it was the heat, the drive or the smell from the kitchen on top of my empty stomach, but I suddenly felt queasy. I went into the lounge and flopped down on the settee while their voices carried on in the hall. They were talking about the work, the pay but I wasn't listening. All I could think about was the two people in my mind's eye who should have been there instead of us. Maybe Jeff and I did look and sound like them but there had been a misunderstanding, a confusion. We weren't supposed to be there at all. That was the one thing I knew.

"Liz, are you all right?" Jeff stuck his head round the door. "We can drive over and meet the farm manager now. Come on." He grabbed my hand and pulled me up.

"The money's good," he whispered, giving me a kiss on the ear. A ring of black spots wheeled just beneath the ceiling and I leant against him to get my balance.

"God, I felt terrible just then."

Jeff put his arm around me and led me to the car. "It's been a long day I know, but like you said, it's going to be fine."

And once we were back on the move, following Peter's Land Rover down the track, with air blowing in through the window I felt much better.

'*I like driving in my car.*' Jeff had switched the radio on full blast and was half singing, half shouting along to the music. '*It's not quite a Jaguar.*'

The main farm buildings were a mile away from the two houses, back over the road and East towards the sea. We pulled up behind Peter in a yard with a green cropstore tower to the right – the one I'd seen earlier, and three long glass greenhouses on the left. There was a barn and storage buildings straight ahead with bags of nitrate piled outside. One of the bags had split and white granules covered the ground. We followed Peter into a shed where a stocky man in a blue boiler suit was rolling a chemical drum across the floor.

"Hey Brian," called Peter and he straightened up and came over to greet us, rubbing the small of his back. He was in his late twenties and he struck me as one of those relaxed but efficient people who are good to work for.

"You must be the new people," he said.

"Give them a quick tour," said Peter who seemed to be in a hurry to leave. He turned to me and Jeff. "If you want to take the work you can come back tonight and start tomorrow, Monday. If you don't fancy it...have a nice life." With that he gave a curt wave, jumped into the Land Rover and screeched off. The tyres kicked up dust as the vehicle bumped and rumbled away into the distance.

"He's all right really," said Brian as though he was apologising for Peter's gruffness, "he's got his fishing and shooting and holidays abroad with his wife. A lot of farmers who inherit aren't that interested in the business and he's one of them. He leaves me to it."

Brian explained that several miles of drainage ditches needed clearing before winter – that would be Jeff's work. In the greenhouses they needed someone to pick salad crops, cut flowers and spray for pests – which would be me. He opened the door to the first greenhouse releasing a pungent blast of humid heat. The plants near the door were sagging with ripe tomatoes. "We've got behind," Brian sighed. "Some of it's even starting to rot."

"Why?" I asked.

"You see all this fallen fruit will need clearing up," he said looking down at the ground. "I suppose we'll have to burn it."

"Why did they go?"

Brian was silent then he met my eyes briefly. "Don't know. I stay out of all that." He shut the greenhouse door and we walked back towards the car.

The sky had clouded over since we arrived, bringing a cool breeze. Fat drops of rain started to splatter down, speckling the dust in the yard with dark spots.

"We'll see you tomorrow morning then." Jeff shook his hand and jangled the car keys.

"Seven o'clock sharp," laughed Brian, obviously pleased. He patted Jeff gently on the back.

"Nice bloke," said Jeff as he put the key in the ignition. Brian walked into the farm office, picked up the phone to make a call and we drove off back to town.

That evening we came back with most of our stuff in black bin bags. Clothes, records, shoes, a couple of mugs and a few bits of cutlery. We nearly missed the turning because the home-made placard had been removed, but I knew the way this time using the cropstore on the other side of the road as a marker. Jeff still had the key to Sky View so we drove straight there.

Someone had been in since we'd left and taken the jacket and bags from upstairs away. There was a smell of bleach and the kitchen floor had been scrubbed, the fridge emptied and cleaned out. No power yet, but the water had been turned on. On top of the fridge was a tray with a plate of sandwiches covered with a cloth, some candles and matches and a note in careful loopy handwriting. "Enjoy your new home! Let me know if you need anything, M."

We unloaded our things and left most of the bags in the two empty rooms upstairs. I went round the house opening windows and Jeff used a knife to prise open the patio doors which gave onto the front garden. The air was fresher after the rain and the cool of the evening crept into the lounge perfumed with honeysuckle and damp earth.

"Once we've cleared that rubbish away, put the fence back up, I'll borrow a lawnmower and we can have a lawn. What do you reckon Liz?. Our own little patch of grass to lie on and stare up at the sky."

Jeff dug a couple of beers out of one of his bags and, as it got darker I put the plate of sandwiches out on the coffee table and lit two of the candles.

"Housewarming party."

I thought about the cramped bedsit we'd left behind and the supermarket job I didn't have to go to any more and I was glad Jeff had persuaded me to come back. As it got dark, we lay on the settee and talked about our plans, how we would stay working there until the Spring and then go travelling, or move to London with the money. Those were the two big dreams. Then Jeff described the sound system he was going to buy, and I thought about the back rent we owed on the bedsit, and the money Dad had lent me which I knew he wanted back.

In the distance I could see the orange haze made by the town's lights, but out here the land was dark as the sea, houses blinking in the distance like scattered ships. The night sky was so clear I couldn't make out the usual shapes at first, they were lost in a shower of stars.

The din of sudden barking bumped me back down to earth. "Bloody dogs," muttered Jeff. Looking across at the other house I saw a light come on in the kitchen, a figure reaching up to bolt the back door.

Jeff's face was lost in the deep shadows thrown by the candles. He had something in his hand.

"What's that?" I asked.

"Dunno," he said holding it up to the light. "I found it down the back of the cushion."

I took it from him. It was made of straw, woven into a tapered shape with a ribbon tied to one end. There was something familiar about it.

"It's a corn dolly isn't it?"

"Oh yeah," said Jeff sleepily.

The chemical taste of orange squash came back to me and I remembered where I'd seen one – in Margaret's kitchen, hanging by its ribbon from one of the cupboard handles.

I sat up, and hugged my knees to my chest feeling the night chill.

"Jeff. Don't you think it's funny that they took the sign away so soon?" It was as if Bethlem Farm had surfaced and sunk back out of sight in the space of one hot afternoon.

"It's done its job now I suppose," said Jeff with a yawn. "They've got what they were after haven't they? The two of us. That was all they wanted."

SUE BUTLER

Eight Poems

Sue Butler grew up in Hertfordshire and now lives in Norfolk.

Giving Alms

Afraid of being poisoned
the ex-minister of State Security ate

nothing but eggs, borrowed
from the prison library only the words

of his hero; shown the news
of a colleague's arrest he read

the headline twice then asked
to be given the sports pages.

Stapled to his file were allegations
that he personally beat the wife

of a comrade's eldest son, was seen
in the city's poorest courtyards,

where he handed out money
from Party funds, not just

to Party members but to anyone
who looked cold.

First Date

They sit in a cafe no different
to the ones back home,

drink a lot, smoke a lot, see
briefly the frozen waves and think

them grey, are bored
by the gulls and the trawlers

red with rust trapped
until April in the ice.

They spend the afternoon
in markets haggling;

tired of each other before
they have even got started.

First Things

At dawn for the sake
of argument though it might
easily be dusk, pigeons at home
in the cupola's intricate

mosaic, each exquisite tile
glazed with copper sulphate and iron.
Stray dogs steal carp
from the courtyard pool,

the onyx inlay of its balustrade
white as the nearby
fields of ripe cotton, so relentless
in their collective thirst

that what was sea is now
steppe; the few trees are ancient,
heavy with pomegranates
and men are bending to prayer.

The Accident

They should have met
out of the rain, he in the obligatory
blue suit, she in a hurry.

He could easily have telephoned,
invented an excuse for a meeting.
Assuming they laughed

at each other's jokes, it is not she
who should be kneeling.
Out early to buy milk she heard

the tram brake and watched closely
by a crowd who think
she is too late, it is more important

than any client's profit, this forcing
the rise, allowing the fall,
this mouth to mouth to mouth.

The Morning of the Putsch

The decorators stop painting to smoke
and a young woman carefully

counts the notes before leading
the tall stranger upstairs; adorning

the hall the pictures done in crayon
show a rainbow, the dome

of the Kazan, tigers at the circus,
one being chased by a clown.

A dying swan jetés across all channels
and from a neighbour's room

the muffled Voice of America reports
soldiers approaching Smolny,

tanks in the Palace Square.
The child draws flowers until

the water boils then helps
his grandmother kill

and scald a small pig, loads
the meat onto a sledge

so they can get it to the market
still warm.

May your hands never be cold

May you always have a coat with buttons
and shoes good enough for the Nevsky,
fresh pork, white bread, Moldavian butter,
quince preserve to sweeten your tea.
May you never have to queue for salt,

your cognac always be Armenian,
your vodka cold and undiluted –
abundant enough to lift depression,
enough left over to share.
May you always wear amber

close to your skin, be free
from tumours and liver complaints,
die quietly at home
long before your son
but not before your mother.

May you never have to live in Baku,
in Kosovo or Grozny,
never have your God insulted,
never have to shoot a man
or have him shoot at you.

May your friends be kind,
your ex-wife not meet a millionaire
or a plumber with Paul Newman looks.
May a fake magician
never saw you in half

and slow and Ukrainian
through the wooden grille,
with moonlight on the canal outside,
may your priest give you absolution
when you tell him what you have just done.

Love Poem for Ugly People

On a morning in Lent so dense
with rain that even with the wipers

going they can not make out
the ocean, they are discussing why

Rembrandt should paint
the prodigal's heel in such detail, hide

and if the miracle is not
that the son came back

but that the father abandoned
all dignity and held him

to his heart. It is a borrowed car
and the flask was bought

in Kharkov on a day much sunnier
than this; the tea steams up

his glasses and when he takes
them off it is a shock

for her to be kissed, to see
his eyes unmagnified.

At Shakrisabz

Here, unless the army is bored with marching,
cleaning rifles or painting General's fences,
picking the cotton is women's work,
like weaving and making pots, tending the house
and the animals. Daughters learn early and accept it.

Waiting to be soldiers sons drink tea and smoke,
lie in the shade until it is cool enough to tell stories
or burn tyres by the road. Through the flames,
they watch my spine curve as I lean to rinse
the soap from my hair, my face, my arms.

Steve Carr has been a paper boy, egg boy, preacher's apprentice, theology student, door-to-door book salesman (Sweden), silver service waiter (Denmark), drama student, sole wiper, warehouseman (Picker), actor, camera assistant, bus boy, telephone salesman, T.E.F.L. teacher (Taiwan), playwright, estate agent, cameraman, managing director and receptionist. Recently, he has become a screenwriter and creative writing student and won the Scriptwriting Bursary this year. He is the father of two girls, Nancy (7) and Mary (4) and is husband to Fliff (35).

1. INT. TOM'S PLACE. DAY.

A mangy bedsit. The detritus on the floor, the unmade bed in the corner, indicative of a young life in a shambles, compounded by the sound of someone trying to tune in a small radio, skipping back and forth over the same stations, but settling on none. JACK, small, pale, 27, sits with the sun on his back in the window, watching someone, wide-eyed, barely concealing his anxiety.

JACK   So…what happened?

TOM, stocky, handsome, scruffy with long blond curls, stands by a kitchen counter, the radio in his hands, ambling through the airwaves, deep in thought.

TOM   So… have you seen Ralph?

A beat.

JACK   No… not for ages.

Cut to:

2. EXT. THE WESTWAY.

A car zooms by and we cut to:

3. INT. THE CAR.

JACK drives out over the Westway. RALPH, 27, tall, scruffy chic, sits in the passenger seat. JACK glances at RALPH who is going over and over things in his head. JACK *takes a drag of his fag and blows the smoke out of the window and mildly shakes his head.*

RALPH   He always liked you.

A moment as this comment settles. RALPH *keeps an eye on* JACK.

RALPH   Did you see the effigies he made of us. You and me and him.
JACK   Me?

Cut to:

4. INT. TOM'S PLACE.

THREE PLASTICINE 'effigies' – more like children's sculptures, not tortured, just sitting like dollies on the mantelpiece. Pan to JACK *who looks at them and then at* TOM.

TOM   This is fucked…

He slams the radio on a counter that separates this kitchen area from the lounge area of the bedsit. He picks up a carving knife and begins unscrewing the back of the radio.

TOM   If either of us had had girlfriends, it wouldn't have happened.
JACK   You think?

Cut to:

5. INT. THE CAR.

JACK *and* RALPH *are laughing. When the laughter subsides.*

RALPH   I'm twenty-seven. I've got to get something going.
JACK   You felt Tom was holding you back?
RALPH   I've got to stop dicking around.

Jack *takes out another cigarette and lights it. He takes a drag. Cut to:*

6. INT. TOM'S PLACE.

Tom *is now dismantling the guts of the radio, piece by piece, laying out the components in front of him.* Jack *stands watching him.*

Tom   Hey! Listen! I'm going on a solo tour. Soon. Maybe
           next week. I might be leaving next week. (*A beat.*) I
           might leave tonight. All the money from the tour
           will go to the starving people... What do you think?
           Good idea? Good idea or what?
Jack   Good idea... Tom...
Tom   Great idea... You see that's what I like about you.
           You're honest.

A beat.

Tom   We were like brothers. When we were kids he
           wouldn't tell me when he didn't want me to come
           round – he'd just go out and then afterwards he'd
           laugh and say he forgot.

Tom *starts laughing.*

Jack   Ralph likes to keep his options open, you know
           that.

Cut to:

7. INT. THE CAR.

Ralph *takes a packet of Rizlas out of his pocket and rips out three.*

Ralph   Did he tell you he was making a machine?
Jack   A machine?
Ralph   So you haven't seen him?
Jack   I've seen him, but...

RALPH	What did you talk about?
JACK	Not much... I didn't really want to bring it up...
RALPH	I was asleep. It was the middle of the night...

Cut to:

8. INT. TOM'S FLAT.

TOM	... It was Christmas Eve. I wanted to talk. So I went down to his room. He was asleep...

Cut to:

9. INT. THE CAR.

RALPH	... I felt this hand on my shoulder, I turned over and there he was with a carving knife in his hand. He said he wanted to talk to me.

10. INTERCUT BETWEEN TOM AND RALPH.

TOM	I'd been doing some work so I had a screwdriver in my hand. He started cracking jokes...
RALPH	... I said, "if it's a talk you want, maybe you should have brought an armchair."
TOM	... I wanted to talk.
RALPH	... I said, "we can talk if you put the knife down. If you want to keep the knife, maybe we could chop vegetables, make a stew"...
TOM	SHUT UP!

A beat.

RALPH	"You want me to talk but you want me to shut up. Make up your mind."

Cut to:

11. INT. TOM'S FLAT.

Tom   This was my last chance.

Jack *sits on the window sill.* Tom *goes on deconstructing the radio.* Jack *looks across to the stereo – it's in pieces.*

Tom   Neighbours called the police.

Cut to:

12. INT. THE CAR.

Ralph   I wanted to get the stash out of the way.

Cut to:

13. INT. TOM'S PLACE.

Tom, *the radio in smaller pieces, in his hands.*

Tom   I felt myself getting smaller and smaller.

Cut to:

14. EXT. THE CAR...

...as it careens by.

Ralph   So, he grabbed the stash and went to the window.

Cut to:

15. TOM'S FLAT.

Tom   "Talk to me!" I said. "Talk to me about what's going on or talk to the police about this."

Tom *tugs at the circuit board ripping it out of the keyboard – the action seems to weaken him. He stops. Cut to:*

16. INT. The Car.

RALPH *lights the joint and breathes in the smoke.*

RALPH   He tried to throw himself out the window.

RALPH *starts laughing. Cut to:*

17. INT. TOM'S FLAT. AS BEFORE.

Tom   … Uncle Tom Cobbly – suddenly the place was surrounded.

The radio now sits disassembled on the counter but TOM *goes on – snipping the wiring into small pieces and laying them out beside it. Cut to:*

18. THE CAR – INTERCUT WITH TOM'S PLACE.

RALPH   By the time the police came, he was gone. It looked like he'd been hypnotised. He knew what he was doing, but it wasn't him doing it. He climbed up onto the roof…

Tom   … It's a great view from up there, you know – all over West London…

RALPH   He started preaching – shouting about the machine he was making, a communication machine.

Tom   The police came up and barged in – then the firemen came up and barged in and they all got to the window, but no one wanted to come up after me. Shit-scared. I had them all shit-scared of me. (*Laughs*) So I told them about the machine.

RALPH   Christ, he really went for it. I admired him for that.

RALPH *stubs out the end of the joint in the ash tray. Cut to:*

19. EXT. TOM'S PLACE. THE ROOF.

A view over West London – Tom seemingly king of all he surveys.

TOM   It was cold up there. Really cold. I could see Ralph was down in the street talking to the fire brigade. That was funny. He just looked so funny down there talking to the fire brigade. I mean Ralph – and the fire brigade, can you imagine it? Comedy, that is.

Cut to:

20. INT. THE CAR.

RALPH   I looked at him up there, by himself and something about it was suitable.

21. INT. TOM'S PLACE.

TOM   I want you to come with me – be in the band with me. Come on tour. Show everyone the machine. What do you say?

JACK   I don't know…

TOM   Hey! Hey! Hey! Listen, listen, listen!

Excitedly, TOM *gathers up a keyboard and switches it on. He plays and sings very badly but with conviction.*

TOM   "Do they know it's Christmas time at all!
Do they know it's Christmas time at all."

JACK *looks on.* TOM *holds the note on 'all' and plays a different note on the keyboard, his grand finale. Finally, he releases the key and stops singing.*

TOM   What do you think? Tell me the truth. You know I've had it with liars, you know? No more lies. What do you really think?

Slight pause.

JACK   Fantastic!
TOM   Fantastic? (TOM *sniggers*.) Liar!

TOM *flips the keyboard over and begins unscrewing the back of it.*
Cut to:

22. INT. THE CAR, AS BEFORE.

A beat. They look at one another.

RALPH   So?

A beat.

JACK   What?
RALPH   What d'you think?
JACK   I don't know what to think.
RALPH   Well, I think none of this would have happened if
either of us had had a girlfriend.

RALPH *pulls on a cigarette.*

RALPH   How's Susan?

A beat.

JACK   She's well, thanks.
RALPH   Good.

Cut to:

23. INT. TOM'S FLAT.

JACK *stands at the door, about to leave.*

JACK   Susan sends her love.

The floor is strewn with electrical items: radios, a keyboard, a toaster, a baby belle oven, an electric guitar, a computer. All of the items have been disembowelled, not smashed up, but taken apart and laboriously laid out in elemental form. The casing sits next to the internal workings and the wiring, each piece of which has been carefully and geometrically arranged next to the device from which it came.

Tom *sits in the middle of it with a carving knife in his hand.*

TOM   Sure... Hey, don't worry about me. When the machine is ready, everything will be fine.

JACK   Great! Good luck with it.

Cut to:

24. EXT. THE CAR.

As it speeds away. Fade to Black.

End.

FRANCES CHAPMAN

from *Ruhe*

Frances Chapman was born in London. She studied English at Cambridge University and worked for several years before starting to write. *Ruhe* is her first novel.

This pen is scratchy. It's old and clogged with curdled inkflake but I'm loath to put it to the back of the drawer and look out a replacement. After all these years it suits my hand and I am rather fond of it. I've grown used to the rasp of nib frotting against fibrous sheet of best laid Conqueror, which accompanies even the briefest billet-doux. Once it would have set my teeth on edge, quite put me off my stroke even.

Gravitational, peristaltic promptings following rapidly from breakfast sent me spinning down the stairs to my watercloset, pausing only to gather a handful of press clippings from the dresser drawer as I passed. A little later – rectified – I've come out here to my favourite seat, where the cats have made a run through the low lavender bushes and wisteria floribunda covers the wall as far as the Sheela-na-gig below the drain pipe. The brazen vestal has hung there for as long as I can remember, more ancient than Avebury and bolder by far than Cerne. She's glued to the spot with a creamy emission of limestone mortar, a dose so fulsome as to ooze through the crook of each out-turned arm. With both hands plunged up to the wrists in her privates, she's ready at a moment's notice to flip out her lights onto the straggling privet beneath.

It's sheltered here by the wall, with just a suspicion of a slight breeze although they tell me it will become keener as the morning wears on. Perhaps I should send for my guernsey, the plumbago-blue one, the one as blue as Isidore's eyes. I abhor draughts. There's nothing to compare with the chill blasts here during the winter months, apart from the invidious damp, that is. As little as a single Michaelmas at Ruhe will age even the perkiest old gamecock by as much as three years. Usually, at least one of us will have been carried off by the cold before the return of spring. At the first sign of a change in the weather, or at the Equinox (being the twenty-third of September), either way, whichever is soonest, we take to our beds and remain there, sometimes even as late as Mayday.

(I have just glanced at the pier glass in the dining room. My plaited straw sunhat has incised a weal upon each temple, very like a crown of thorns.)

In retrospect, this pattern of collective confinement could be said to be partly responsible for the rise of Cyprien. It permitted him just the minutest cavity in which to insinuate his vile self. He was thirteen when he first entered this house. I concealed myself in the boot room and watched from behind the curtain as they led him through the gate. Foundling boy, with his small hard face grooved like a pill – the long upper lip with its pronounced septum – and those fine nostrils pinched and white against the bright blood flaring in his cheeks. I looked on him then and pitied him his loss.

During that first winter I often called on Cyprien to read to me and, in time, came to enjoy the hours we spent together, even to relish what was familiar and dear to me in the timbre of his voice. I taught him to speak softly into my good ear, bending slightly from the left of my pillow, where he always sat. And even though his vocabulary was somewhat lacking back then, seed catalogues and almanacs being almost the only reading matter available amongst the gardeners, he made astonishing progress. I took considerable pleasure in introducing him to: the correct mode of pronunciation during the ages of Ronsard and Villon; a smattering of Mandarin; early Sumerian; what little Cajun I happened to pick up from the Louisiana pot boy; some dockside argot – diligently gleaned in the stews of Deptford; and, last of all, semaphore.

Every day, soon after lunch, I sent down to the kitchens for him, and without fail, he would quit the scallions and the purple artichokes, the chicory and the kale, and come and perch on my bed bundled up in a muffler and two malodorous overcoats eloquently telling of peat and fust. As he read, his voice issued murmurously forth from within the many corm-like layers of cloth – hopsack, oilskin and wool – which encased his slight torso and enabled him to move about the frozen corridors in relative comfort[1]. The technique of compressing words between narrowed lips – an exercise which compels the listener to crane

---

[1] A stone is but a bulb of intransigence, about which countless grains of insoluble, brittle matter gather, coiled one upon the other, sealed within a infinitude of skins.

towards the locutor – is the accepted method for discourse during the winter. If at all possible, the practice of opening one's mouth extravagantly wide, is to be discouraged lest the breath turn to hoar-frost in one's throat. The wind across the estuary is sharp and strong enough to slice a man in two, to make shale of his tears or congeal the words on his tongue. In a lesser incarnation, where it enters by the broken panes of Ruhe, it is sufficiently formidable to deter precise enunciation. But we managed tolerably well he and I; he, done up all the while, within his several greatcoats and I beneath the pile of ancient furs[2] surmounting the hump of my long body within the bed.

In common with the rest of us, Isidore spent his winters in hibernation, but in keeping with his position as son of the house, it was imperative that he be doubly insulated from the cold. Each season, up until the onset of puberty, Isidore retired to bed swaddled in goosefat and wrapped round with undergarments as dense and closeknitted as felt. On four consecutive springs during the formative years of three to six, when the time came for him to leave his truckle bed, it was discovered that months of inactivity and the generous application of alternate layers of dripping and bandaging had deprived him of the ability to walk. Relearning that particular motor skill was always a painful process.

The first bathing of each new year saw Isidore skimmed of his winter basting. Scraping the gross substance from his armpits, the housemaid would notice how his skin had grown soft and white as suet. If you should be tempted to stick your finger into him then, she thought, the indentation would remain like a dimple in the dough. Although the fat had been applied in a thick coating which covered him from head to foot and wrapped in place with bales of undershirts and singlets, it was always found to have migrated to line all the creases and folds of his body. This residual matter was duly scraped from his groin and other places onto clouts and rags, later discarded for burning. In a similar way that ambergris[3] will hold fragrance, the goosefat absorbed Isidore's

---

[2] The spoils of a trapping expedition mounted years since by some or other great uncle, which, incidentally, contributed greatly to the decimation of a certain sub-species of sphagnum-grazing moose indigenous to the Arctic circle.

[3] An ash-grey substance originating in the intestine of the spermaceti whale. Used in the manufacture of perfume as a fixer for scent.

individual odour and the abandoned rags become for all the world, a kind of wraith Isidore to confuse the dogs.

Winter is a time of heightened perception for the dogs at Ruhe. Additional smells and stenches come into being and those already in existence are ripened to a pitch of maddening deliciousness. By late March we're all pretty much ripe as cheeses, humming about the house each with our own specific home-grown stink, the work of teeming, industrious bacteria over many, many months, which pop and fizz beneath our clothes. But by sloughing off our filth with the coming of spring, we humans put a stop to the intricate and complex messages transmitted thereby to the canine nose. Such intelligences, engendered by filth, add a further dimension to the world of the senses as only a dog may experience it – by smell – and that world must revert to a certain flatness when the human population of Ruhe returns to walk its corridors, clean once more. Missing one of our dimensions, to the dogs we must seem to have as little substance as cardboard cutouts in a child's pasteboard theatre.

With the warmer weather comes the task of airing rooms in preparation for summer visitors. Colonies of rats and spiders are, at this time of year, routinely cleansed from the piles of dust and scraps of discarded food that collect under beds and in the corners of rooms. Soon the house's inhabitants begin to emerge, displaced from their long internment in dusty bedrooms by the unceasing toil about them. Forth they come, grey-faced and liberally blossoming with bed sores, drawn in one body towards the bathrooms and the laundries. It is a time when those over-wintering at Ruhe may at last strip away their outer coverings and it is not uncommon to see the assembled number taking advantage of the seasonal warmth by sporting naked in the open air, blanched as celeriac root. In every bedroom, waxen bodies, leopard-blotched with ulcerous points and dashes, sparkle in long-neglected mirrors.

Consider then, how affecting a sensation it is to be, all at once, unclothed. The revelation is all the more poignant if, like Isidore, one has spent one's tender years stitched into fibrous, pricklesome vestments. It is altogether quite possible to become unhinged by the novelty of the situation. I myself, have seen them, careening, as if the very devil were after them, down halls and passageways alike, with their pale feet slapping on the bare boards and linoleum, thrilling all the *while to the prickling of their naked skins. How foreign are our bodies to us then! Indeed, by spring, one is infinitely more familiar with the fleshy construction of the Borodino nudes in the long gallery, the pulleys and levers that operate their corporeal mechanisms, than with the component parts of one's own physical make-up.*

Copulation is not the least of our problems during the winter months. To be brief, it is precisely managed (that is, if one is set on the idea and simply won't be put off) and carried out with as much nicety as can be mustered, amongst our pungent number at that time. Those who can bear to run the risk of overwhelming, or of being overwhelmed, do so, those that can't, stint themselves. The place smells like a tuppenny flophouse mattress for six months of the year, but there is little to be done about it.

A shrike is calling somewhere over the estuary. At the point where the land ends and the broad bourn widens out to the sea, stands a short, wooden jetty. To either side, decaying wrecks of hulks and barges have been used to shore up the riverbank where subsidiary streams flow and threaten to erode them. Little islets of marled-green alluvium have formed between these fast-running tributaries.

Here and there, at the water's edge below the strand, solitary mooring posts, blackly encrusted with weed and river slime, poke up through shallow, brown pools which collect in the dips and depressions of the estuary bed. Further upstream towards Ruhe, the river is silted and impassable by boat, although it was once possible to row from the lake as far as the sea without once setting foot on land.

It is dangerous to walk on the mud flats at this time of year.

It's always very windy out on the foreshore; today there's a north-easterly. If I turn my face into the blast and narrow my streaming eyes (they are sometimes a little rheumy I know, the merest breeze will make them water so), I can just see a figure standing some distance away by the sandbanks. I can't quite make the fellow out.

This is an odd, anyhow, time of day; too bright to turn in and yet too late to start anything afresh. As the rigours of the approaching twilight hours are best held at bay with a warming drink and a choice cigar, might I propose that we return to the house and furnish ourselves with a noggin or two. Take my hand, the going is inordinately slippy hereabouts. That's right. Your fingers are uncommonly cold, but firm, and smooth as paste. Let us pause a moment. Let us, as it were, allow an angel to pass. Yes, that's good.

I believe it may be Florialis at the sluice (poor Florialis, my very own Priapus, guardian of vineyards and gardens). He has one of the dogs with him. Cyprien, whom you've met of course, is his son (although Cyprien wouldn't thank me for that particular observation). However, you will no doubt already have guessed something of the nature of the relationship from the quarts of spleen he decants on the subject.

Florialis, my head gardener (as he then was), brought his motherless boy – Cyprien – to live at Ruhe, where he was raised in the bosom of a bucolic fellowship. The company of under-gardeners, who shared amongst them the burden of his care and upbringing, did so out of compassion for his semi-orphaned state. I like to think of the arrangement as something rather along the lines of a confederacy of bachelors, even though, you understand, gardening as a profession by no means precludes relations of an intimate nature. Undoubtedly, horticulture is a somewhat priestly calling, but it is in no way at odds with the antediluvian dictate to act, and perpetually re-enact, the gross deed of union. I for one, have never required celibacy of my nurserymen.

Now, I hope you won't be offended (and this is very much by-the-by), but I have always thought you possessed the most lovely speaking voice. You must have been blessed with an extraordinarily beautiful palate.

Don't forget your bicycle. It is lying there by the rushes.

The evening sky was incarnadine, much as it is now. Scarlet bark in rags and ribbons, peeled from the frail birches in the arboretum where a murmuration of starlings gathered restively in the wand-thin branches, croaking out the hour. Urien, peaceable and alone, strolled beneath the high, red brick wall which encloses a section of the garden to the north of the house. The wall is bowed, age-old and crumbling, lavish with dog roses run rampant, and topped by a self-seeded bank of saplings and gorse-like, ground-hugging bushes. Above them, a shallow inclination, thick with ivy, rises up to meet the level of the lawn beyond.

"Great G—!" At once, a shout went up from the direction of the Dial Garden. Within the house[4], Isidore, alerted by the cry (and glad of a diversion from his lessons, no doubt), flung open the casement and craned from the window seat, primer in hand. I hastened to extinguish my Players Navy Cut in the nearest ashtray (an especial favourite of mine, filched from the Cafe Royal in London's Piccadilly) and leaving the fringed velveteen couch beneath the aquatint of de Sade (from the Charenton portrait[5]), came to stand – one pale hand flat upon Isidore's forearm – at the open window.

Heavy, unseasonable rain had of late, caused the earth to open up in several places, leaving many craters and fissures in its wake. In the Dial Garden, subsidence had split the circular stone pond (unleashing little becks and rills, which bled fiercely into the surrounding loam) and cast the dial at an oblique angle upon the menhir, threatening to disgorge the delicate chronometer lodged within the great mechanism. A troupe of gardeners had duly been dispatched to set the dial in place. However, greasy from the treacly ooze underfoot, which splashed into eyes and ears and made all flesh slick as scales, they struggled, fitfully and with little success, to find a purchase on that glorious facsimile of the Jesuit, Franciscus Linus' 'pyramidical diall'.

Together, they hauled upon the guys – one against another – apportioning the load equally between all hands. Until, growing suddenly heedless of those others round about him, Florialis placed the tip of his frail scapula at the immense iron foot and in one movement, took the full weight of the dial upon himself. Directly, each man stood delivered of his load with nothing but a flaccid rope resting between his mud-streaked palms.

The vast instrument, unstable now and tipping on its narrow rim, staggered once and then dropped, straight and heavy.

---

[4] Every house is a receptacle for our memories. We make them in our own image; each dwelling may be as bitter or as sweet as we please.

[5] 'The Divine Marquis' (Donatien Alphonse Francois, Marquis de Sade, 1740-1814). There is no such portrait in existence.

Urien entered the garden at a run. Standing alone beneath the plunging missile, Florialis tore himself from the smooth sides of the obelisk and stepped back, but no more than a pace, before the force of the blow knocked him down, the filigreed bronze gnomon[6] (a purely decorative and fanciful feature, and no more) putting out the eye from his head. The dial dashed upon the stones beneath.

On a large, white handkerchief which I took from your pocket, I wiped the blood from your face where it burst from that terrible wound. And I knew then that my heart had left my breast and beat elsewhere, far beyond, sounding out a hard and regular rhythm (as of the eructation of a chestnut gelding as it rocks with its heels upon the packed earth in a slow, suspended canter).

I felt nothing but the weight of you upon my hands. I saw nothing but a dying sun, and a grimy swan upon the water.

One of the many heavy iron bands which encased the timepiece had crushed his brow inflicting immeasurable damage to the temporal lobe[7]. An injury of such gravity, as I understand it, is almost certain to result in hallucinations, mania and in extreme cases, fugue states and seizures. When he returned many months later, his eye was saved, although the sight in it remained considerably dimmed.

Isidore has his mother's eyes. They are of a type, sufficiently large and blue and shining to have elicited a deep and resonating response in the soul of a Victorian painter specialising in subjects of a sentimental nature. Dividing the cupid's bow of his mouth is a thin white scar, evidence of a slight

---

[6] The stylus of a sundial, indicating the hours of the day. (A vain and futile thing: there is no stable point of reference to be had in all this world.)

[7] Vinegar and brown paper are often cited as particularly efficacious when it comes to the mending of broken crowns; vinegar to take away the sting and brown paper to stop the bleeding. As an impromptu remedy, it does work, but only on a superficial level. Vinegar and brown paper can never make scattered wits whole again.

hare lip corrected soon after birth, some nineteen years ago now; corrected that is, but not entirely erased from the several, smooth planes of his face. How provoking against the splendour of the eyes – this vertical bisection of the mouth. How imperfectly perfect. He is wearing a coat the colour of bloom on a plum. Cyprien has already pronounced upon it.

"Wonderful how corruption is. The nimbus of iridescence about the scales of a two-day old salmon, verdigris on a cupola, the infloration of certain micro-bacillus in the gut and the blood which flew to stain your cheek where I laid my hand upon it... Now... I should like you to lick the sole of my shoe."

Isidore moves down the long, flagged hallway and out into the garden through the buttery door. In the cool of the early summer morning, he chooses the lavender path and exits by the raised walk, where, on a low, ornate bench beneath a copper-leaved beech, Araminta waits for him. Waving away a somnolent bee, he lowers his splendid moleskins to perch above a virulent outcrop of lichen which covers the seat, his thighs goosepimpling on contact with the chill of the stone and the thrilling proximity of his beloved.

From her pocket, Araminta takes a small, abalone cigarette case and a rolled-gold, feather-weight lighter and, holding them out, smiles beatifically into his face with all the airless force of her glamour. Isidore feels his heart drop from his breast. Far below them, a gardener issues abruptly from a clump of oshers and pauses, momentarily, beside a tulip tree in ravishing bloom, before moving on in the direction of the lake. Expelling a stream of pale blue smoke from both nostrils, Isidore reads aloud from a cloth-bound pamphlet with scarlet stitching at the spine: "*The Principles Of Infibulation: A Practical Guide.* Chapter one..."

Isidore was born in the Yellow Room at Ruhe. His mother, a woman with a fierce and unflagging passion for bezique, had just reached across the baize to snatch up the long-anticipated queen of spades, mate to her jack of diamonds, when an unconscionable pain auguring the birth of her one and only son, struck her down. And so, with the turn of a card Isidore entered this den of thieves, a squalling, scarlet thing atop a pile of tumbled, rust-splotched playing cards (none of them, as it happened, valued at less than a seven) lying face-up, face-down upon the floor where they had dropped from her hands onto the turkey rug below.

From the first there was little affection or regard between mother and son. Indeed, a few months after the birth, Isidore's dam quit her home for the gaming boards of Paris, Berlin and Copenhagen, accompanied by a singularly muscular luggage-bearer and two spanking new decks of cards, maintaining all the while, to anyone who would listen: "What an abomination is man and, worse still, his propensity for begetting."

From thence (and thereafter, at least twice a year, when little or no money remained), she returned to the orchards of Kent, to her mother's farm, to roost among the boughs heavy with apple blossom, there to await the maturation of a further clutch of her late grandpapa's stocks and bonds.

Meanwhile, Isidore spent his infancy cushioned in the laps of a succession of peripatetic aunts and various other female relatives, most of whom were imminently continent-bound or just returned from thence, in accordance with the waxing and waning of the social season. The tidal flow of feminine flesh coincided exactly with the advent of 'the bachelors', (a mish-mash of male relations and numerous miscellaneous acquaintances besides) who regularly descended en-masse, at the same time each year, in order to partake of the excellent shooting and coursing to be had at Ruhe. Drawn in turn, by the irresistible pull of this seasonal migration of aunts to the house, the bachelors came as much to woo, as to sport and play. At such times Ruhe came to signify no more than the point on a graph where x meets y chromosome.

Isidore was weaned on butterfly kisses and candied caresses, and bathed in the light of many adoring eyes in a great variety of different shapes and colours. Not one cousin or aunt stayed long enough to forge any semblance of a bond between herself and her very temporary charge. The call of the night boat, the romance of Florence, Rimini or Venice, the urge to snuffle up the lingering rich odours and spoors of years gone by, won out every time, proving a far stronger lure than the needs of any infant boy.

To what number of bosoms has Isidore been clasped, both meagre and ample, but each one rendered similarly unbending and unsympathetic by that intractable structure of whalebone which then comprised the contemporary female undergarment. It is hardly surprising therefore, that the sensibilities of the young Isidore – a hostage to the romanticism of foreign travel – stretched out as thin as a wire between aunt and succeeding aunt, became aggravated and inflamed to such a degree that no amount of kindliness on anybody's part, neither family, friends nor domestics, could entirely banish the boy's unhappiness. It was by these means that, to his misfortune, Isidore learnt the unhappy tendency of clutching to himself whatever might come his way. Thus, it is entirely unsurprising that his nature is now rather hollowed out and what little remains is nearly all sugar coating.

Ruhe has countless bathrooms and even more attendant dressing rooms and anterooms which abut, adjoin and border them. The bachelors moved in herds through rooms such as these, congregating where smoke, expunged from the fresh pink lungs of the young men, lent the air the colour and consistency of treacle-syrup. Here they played at whist and poker and indulged in other peculiarly sedentary and masculine pastimes, their hides damply respiring and pungent from earlier and more vigorous pursuits chiefly involving the delights of bat and ball and horse flesh.

Some of these former gathering places are for instance, no bigger than a walk-in linen press or a landing between one flight of steps and the next, where one might pause awhile to smoke a companionable cigarette or even, perhaps, discuss the latest cut in breeches. There is nothing to distinguish them as rooms as such, except occasionally a fire grate or surround surmounted by a single blue and white Chinese vase or a delicate ormolu clock, whispering the hour to no-one in particular.

Cyprien meets Isidore in 'non-rooms' just like these which constitute the caesura of the house, spaces punctuating the endless passage of suites and chambers, affording a moment in which to catch one's breath before the next grand statement, tricked out in once bright gilding and garlands of plaster fruit and flowers. At stone sills and long-vacated window seats, they are accustomed to encountering one another, affecting as always, expressions of mock surprise or pique.

Isidore has discovered Cyprien – fruit of that fatal insertion amidst the whiting – sitting on the low sill in the alcove where the maids pause to rest the weight of their baskets before passing on to the laundries and drying rooms. Cyprien holds a cigarette between spatulate fingers, yellowed by nicotine. On his left hand he wears a ring, a thick golden band set with chips of apple-green chrysoprase. Looking up, he shrugs the hair from his eyes; it is now quite long enough to be thought disreputable and, of late, has taken to falling hyacinthine above his collar, in tendrils and thick, ashen coils.

Later, when they part, Cyprien lights a fresh cigarette, scraping with a chipped thumbnail at a transparent plastic lighter emblazoned with the logo of a major petrol company. At the sudden pain in his wrist, the scene of a mere moment before re-assembles itself in his mind. Taking a book from his pocket he starts to read: "Donatien Alphonse Francois loved chocolate almost as much as he loved his own will and it is well known that he desired his will above all other things. Doomed to be thwarted in much during his life, he achieved notoriety for having failed to secure his ultimate satisfaction and for the years of incarceration followed."

The rooms above the stables were sometimes used to accommodate the overflow of young male visitors to the house. Although commodious, Ruhe is not sufficiently large to adapt to the needs of a score or more of high-spirited youths, not to mention their accompanying valets, factotums and gentlemen's gentlemen, plus all the equipment and accoutrements deemed necessary to the life of a young blade. The stableblock is set at a convenient distance from the house, which was especially fortuitous when it came to filtering out the din that more often than not followed a late dinner.

Lodged in their eyrie above the stables, the bachelors disported themselves in Rabelaisian fashion; declaiming Kipling on the terrace and playing noisily at Cavalry and Indians in the shrubbery below the long gallery. This rutting tide generated a substantial effluvia: detachable cuffs and collars; studs and silk socks; books in morocco and calf; meerschaums discarded in ashtrays; half-smoked coronas stubbed out in coffee cups; be-smudged letters concealed in sock drawers, and mattresses dragged out into the gardens on warm evenings and left to dampen in the early morning dew. Its coming washed through the house and into the grounds beyond, leaving behind quantities of driftwood in the way of corks and emptied bottles and a high water mark of discarded chicken carcasses and beef bones.

Striding out with long loins, operating their large knee and elbow joints jerkily like so many nut crackers snapping open and shut, the bachelors returned from dinner across the ornamental gardens. Bellowing and whooping, they brushed scent as they passed from fronds of lavender which fell across their path and disposed of butts and wrappings beneath the precision-trimmed yew hedges[8]. Back to their rooms they flowed, to rest awhile and allow for the transubstantiation of red mullet, slices of perfectly pink lamb and fruit sorbet into prime young flesh. Here, divested of the plumage of the evening suit, reclining in chairs or on rugs and cushions carelessly flung to the ground, one may have encountered a great multiplicity of complexions, characters and tastes. To think of all those agile-throated young bloods, quaffing and swearing; what a diverse cross-section of manhood, what a genetic pick-and-mix. A whole stable-full of possibilities indeed[9].

---

[8] It's an interesting point worth noting that the Romans were not at all agreeable to the use of yew as hedging material nor, indeed, for any other purpose, associating it with death and mourning. At the very least they considered it an unlucky tree. Despite this and the fact that yews are most commonly found in graveyards, I value them for their prodigious growth (sometimes as much as six inches per year) which is a particularly beneficial attribute when it comes to topiary.

[9] There are some plants that cast their seeds on the wind in the form of little parachutes and some with hooks and hairy burrs to catch on what or whomsoever may be passing. Either way, dissemination is achieved by flux.

Isidore stands at the foot of the stairs as his father climbs laboriously – with much cracking of knee-joints – up to the second landing. Here, between a Utrillo and a Balthus, both corrupted by the same milky patina of mildew, hangs a group portrait of a number of bachelors who frequented the house many decades before, resplendent and glowing against the brilliant sky of several generations ago. For an instant, as Urien passes by, Isidore glimpses his father – an old man now, and ornamented with the enormous, pendulous ears of the aged, male homo sapiens – superimposed upon the saturnine youth of his younger self. Suddenly tremulous, Isidore grasps the banister for support.

NUMAIR CHOUDHURY

from *Babu*

Numair Choudhury, was born in 1975 in Bangladesh. He has studied and loved Creative Writing in Oberlin College, Ohio. This piece is from a novel he is working on. He says the extract is "a bit of a hodge podge, *too much, too quickly*, but then again, so is life…"

The beginning was where he would always get stuck and since, in a way, this is a book about the beginnings of him, let us admit the difficulty of beginnings. 'The Exopision', as Mr. Rahman, his fifth grade literature teacher, wrote in theatrical waves of red chalk, is the most important and 'Highly Impressionable' stage of the story, second only to 'The Climax'. Maybe if Babu had known that Mr. Rahman had never really completed his university degree, but had paid three hundred takas for the diploma that got him the job of lecturer, he might have been a little cynical. But cynicism was something that came much later to Babu, so he obediently jotted down, in his terrible handwriting, *Exopision – very imp.* But in many ways, Mr. Rahman was teaching him something beyond literature, something that transcended their Ahmed's English Course book. Mr. Rahman taught Babu the fundamentals of the political career that later, much after the advent and demise of cynicism, was to come to him. And, anyway, since no teacher in Dhanmondi Boys read anything other than the beginnings and endings of fifth grade essays, Mr. Rahman was also teaching him the survival tricks of eleven year-olds.

Well, enough about beginnings. Since Babu needs no introduction in this day and age, let us get away from the bones of the matter to the proverbial meat in his much celebrated autobiography – to the light brown flesh of a nine pound baby:

I was born incompletely on March 4, 1971 in Dhaka Medical College, my mother's labour punctuated with the gunshots of Pakistani Army troops as they gunned down university professors, students, night watchmen. Incompletely, I stress, because my still-born twin sister had exited months earlier, murdered by our own father who had punched pregnant amma in a drunken rage. Spared by fate and the anciently mysterious means of selective birth, I arrived in a world fraught with the dangers a Bengali-speaking population faced. But since I initially spoke no tongue other than that of the infantile, I survived my tumultuous beginnings.

Here, dear reader, I must enclose the controversial article printed in *The Morning Star* just three years ago, in the Christian year of 2016 and in our Islamic 1436.

Babu a Fraud!

A shocking fact has been discovered: Babu was not, as commonly believed and clearly stated in his book, born on 4th March 1971, but exactly a year earlier. A young budding sleuth from our paper found hospital records of the miscarriage of Babu's twin, dated 12th November 1969. This would mean that the twin could not have been due in March 1971, but a year earlier. Further investigation has revealed that Dr. Kamal Hossain widely revered for being the hand that brought Babu into this world was sick with jaundice during the month of March 1971. When contacted about the possibility of a cover-up as to Babu's real birthdate, Dr. Hossain's near family has refused to answer.

A photocopy of Babu's first passport (printed below) clearly shows that the original date of 4-3-70 has been scratched out and replaced with 4-3-71. The change was made on 26th June 1981. A confession has been obtained from Mhd. Fakruddin Alam who was Assistant Director of Immigration and Passports at that time. Mr. Alam, hailing from Gopalganj, has admitted in his statement that on occasions he and his colleagues wrongly authorized the 'correction' of dates of birth for a small fee. He is currently being held in remand at Central Jail.

A committee, organized by leader of the Opposition, Sayeeda Anwar, is currently pressing for a withdrawal of the Civil Service Medallion for Public Service awarded to Babu in 1998. As Begum Anwar stated at a public rally attended by thousands: "He deceived us all, the nation, the people, the Civil Service, into believing that he was

something that he was not. The great Babu took our trust
and laughed behind our backs, and anyway, what's all
this medallion business? My son has been in the service
for three years already and he works very hard too."

And so, you must understand my plight. Am I to believe this
most shocking of long-earthed facts? Is our beloved Babu a… oh
the word does catch in my throat, a fraud? But how was
the poor man to know of an act committed by his parents
when he was just a wee boy? And the souls of our noble
intellectuals did they really…? Or is it all a lie? To think
that what was probably a mother's concern for her son's
performance in the Matric Examination could throw history
into such a fine mess! It is like watching what we know as
truth, pass through a prism, only to fragment into a gradation
of rumours, lies and dreams. One can only wonder if the reverse
is true, if one can somehow create light out of all the filth they
are chucking about.

And truth: does it really lie in the ear of the beholder, in the
mouth of the teller? I have attempted to contact the young
journalist who discovered the hospital records, but *The Morning
Star* has been most uncompromising, in fact threatening, about
the whole affair. Their attitude has once again thrown me into
doubt about the feasibility of this study on Babu. It seems as if
nowadays, nobody appreciates a little bit of questioning. But, as
my own mother used to say, we must persevere, my little
train will take on the hill. I can do it, I can do it… More from
the autobiography:

*It is no small coincidence that the moment the most intellectual
of Bengalis met their premature fates marked my birth. Of course,
along with them were university darwans, cleaners, cooks and
gardeners, as well as a helping of the beggars that slept on campus
grounds. It is as if the diverse spirits cut adrift by the well-aimed
bullets of Pathans, Sindhis and Punjabis, found their way to the
hospital, and jostled about for space, frightening amma into ejecting me
from her. Apart from the numerous adult voices that invaded my
privacy, I registered one similar to mine in the background; more
specifically loud bawls of baby surprise. But this voice, unlike the*

others, for reasons initially unknown to me, was familiar and one I readily welcomed.

This I did by responding with my not insignificant soprano, one heard by my father waiting in the hallway, causing him to leap at a passing nurse. Sputtering oaths and dribbling betel juice, he frightened her into calling the doctor out. "Sir, sir, congratulations! A boy. Quite a voice on him too." He extended his hand, but suddenly noticing my father's shabby attire, he remembered that my birth expenses were government-funded and that my family was not likely to hire his services again. Dr. Hossain's smile froze, he withdrew his hand and excused himself, leaving my father with a suspicion that the sudden change in the doctor's demeanour was due to a flaw in me that the kindly man could not bring himself to articulate. This belief stayed with my father well into my thirties.

And my mother? She cried softly when they handed me to her, smiled when my fists grabbed at the nothings in the air, and loved me twice as much as reasonable – her love for my dead sister enveloping me, drenching the very air I grasped. This double love has been with me all my life; it is the spring in my walk, the ring in my laugh; it is the fibre of my resolve, the shimmer in my eye.

Here we can see where all the talk started about Babu's sanity, or should I say, his actuality. The rumours about him being infused with the ideas of famous thespians and economics professors, being too full of maternal love, and the spicy skills of canteen cooks, the verbosity of desperate beggars. Of course his professed connection with his dead twin did not help, but the most bizarre of all, the coup d'état, the icing on the already-too-sweet cake, was the whole water thing:

I was fourteen when it first happened. A few of us – Rubel, the Hindu, Munna, Johnny Walker, were in the Ramna Park lake. Munna claimed that he was peeing into the water so we kept a safe distance from him. As I did not know how to swim (yes, in the world's largest delta, prone to the most devastating floods in the world, there are Bengalis who have never had to learn), I stayed in the shallow area. Inevitably I found myself in a yellow stretch of extra-salty fluid and froze. My mouth pursed with the offending stuff, I contemplated furiously. Suddenly and distinctly, I heard Munna giggling furiously and then... a mixture of voices, male and female, speaking in various dialects. But there was nobody there but the five of us. No! Four: Munna at that moment was actually not in the lake, the others had forced him to the bushes to relieve himself. And there were definitely no women there; ladies could not afford the scandalous luxury of baring all as we did. In confusion I swallowed what was in my mouth and ran out screaming.

At the time I did not think much of it. I did not even mention it to Shampa when we spoke that night. I was inclined to put it down one of those delusions I had heard that eaters of excrement experience. But it was a delusion that I could not get rid of – the voices kept returning: once when I fell into a muddy puddle; once when someone balanced a bucket on the door of the boys bathroom in school. Fearing mental derangement, I finally admitted all to Shampa, who, much to my relief, was not shocked: "Yes Babu, it is strange, but what you must understand is that because of me and our connection, you have the ability to hear things others cannot. Your mind is open to the mute voices that surround us, in fact, that lie in us. Think of this as a new book or, rather, a never-ending album, one that you can play whenever you want and turn off too. Think of all the gossip you could pick up! Anyway, it should be much more educational than the Iron Maiden rubbish you normally listen to."

So I started to practise, to listen. It was as if the more pure the water was, the clearer the thoughts came across. In semi-solids I faced a brick wall of voices, compounded to impossible hardness. The longer that the fluid had been in the body of an individual the greater the number of thoughts I would receive. And the larger the quantity of liquid, the clearer the thoughts could be heard. In little amounts I might hear snatches of mental perambulations or strings of words. The further back in time the source went, the more difficult it was to understand what they were saying, the words they used, their dialects. I would also encounter different languages. Water comprises 70% of the human body. In blood, semen, pus, tears, sweat, mucus, saliva, urine, we exchange it every day. Through the very air we breathe, we inhale and exhale vapour. Winds, rivers, living and dead forms, spread themselves and their water in every direction. So, in a sense, at the age of fourteen, I was the most cosmopolitan man in history. This is of course assuming that I was the only one to have ever received this gift. We all contribute to what water carries, just as we draw from its experience.

But apart from these obvious facts, water has always had a special place in the Bangladeshi heart. Rivers criss-cross and zig-zag all over our monsoon land. The yearly floods leave either a boon of rich soil or a curse of mud. Typhoons, hail storms, giant waves decide where our fortunes fall. They give us hydroelectric energy. The beauty of water, its ferociousness, its love, its unpredictability, these have charmed us for centuries. Water takes the shape of its container; it charts the powers that play on it; on the surface it shows us its agitation. But, much like time, it is neutral. It transmits fairly, never taking sides, but rampantly open to influence. Water has as many appearances and expressions as there are forces in the universe.

I feel maybe I am showing too much, too soon. Too much controversy too quickly. Such is the nature of the reality surrounding our Babu. Little is known per se. At this point I must interject, yes, admit, that for most that knew him and, of course, for the hundreds of millions who love him, Babu was just an ordinary human being. A lovely man, they would say. But there are others, who only judge him from not so lovely actions.

My work bears a striking similarity to a visa application process. Nowadays, even we Bangladeshis have the luxury of applying by mail, though some say this is just to make it easier for the concerned authorities to refuse us, without having to deal with baleful stares or, even worse, hair-clutching and chest-beating.

The similarity: in an application you have to send a stamped, self-addressed envelope so that they can mail back your passport. So, one has first to weigh the self-addressed envelope (with the passport inside) and then insert this in the larger envelope which contains the other material that they keep and this is in turn weighed by the Post Office. So you pay for your passport twice.

In writing about Babu, I have many little envelopes to weigh, each one enclosing a bit of his identity, before inserting them and sending them out, in the bigger picture. Just the same, smaller envelopes of others' impressions of him will come back to me in applause or, more probably, condemnation. And they, the world, you too, in fact, my dear reader, keep something back, as I pay twice for who I am and what I am doing: once to Babu's memory and once to you.

To be fair to Babu, I will show you some of his work from before his heart broke with the world's response to realism. His pieces, he said, were the voices that water brought him and even if we accept that, in mediating and choosing voices, Babu gives us little glimpses of himself:

Rabia

Every morning I use the thumb and first two fingers of my right hand to pleat my sari six times before tucking it in against my waist. This is when I ready my mind for the day's work. Each pleat is essential to me; everything in my life falls perfectly in place between them. If I am in a hurry or let my attention wander, the folds will be crooked and the cloth will slip under my foot as I walk. Or maybe the knot will become a hard lump pressing into my side. On these days I know that things will not go well.

Obedience. Always keep your ears open for the bell above the masala cupboard. When it rings, leave whatever you are working on and run upstairs with your tray. When you run, do not slap your feet heavily on the floor like the buffalo that you are, step quietly. When you buy your paan, make sure there is no jorda inside, I don't care how much you like it. Don't ask me why. These things are not told to you for a reason. So what if you have cleaned the store room? Do it again, sweep it properly. In your hands even the newest broom lets dirt through. Don't argue with Selim Bhai if he wants his cha earlier today. Do it for him and don't you dare screw your face into the ugliness that I have been trying to make you hide, but you never listen.

The first is most important. The rest have to be the same in broadness so that they all look like one. And if the first is too thick, then there will not be a respectable amount of cloth left at the end to throw over my shoulder and cover me.

Humility. When you play with Apa, do what she wants. Remember that you live in their house and that you eat what they let you eat. Don't ever let me see you forgetting yourself and the filth you come from. If it were not for Shahib's generosity, you would be one of those whores on the street corner, fighting with the rickshawallahs. But that's probably what you want to be, huh? Never look a man in the eye. Allah made us weaker so that we listen for our own good. Did I hear that you raised your voice at Jalal Bhai? That you raised your voice at the man who took care of you when you were small? And you ask why your father left! We will never find you a husband, not with all the proud airs you give yourself, disagreeable woman that you are.

The second comes easier. After folding, I pinch it tightly against the first, using my thumb and third finger. With my left hand I pull a fresh stretch from the cloth lying coiled on the floor, waiting to twist itself around me.

Assiduity. There is very little soap today. Use the softer rock to wash the clothes, but make sure you get all the marks out. Are you listening for the bell? You must improve your firni. What kind of girl cannot make a decent firni? And Jalal tells me they have eaten the same bhaji three times this week. Learn new ones. The cat has left shit all over the entrance. Run now before Shahib sees it, but clean the floor the right way, squat on your heels; don't wet your sari, you're lucky they gave you one at all. Apa wants her tea, make sure you take her the hot chutney. You cannot take your day off this month, they are having an Iftar party on Friday. Always check the spoons before giving them to guests.

By the third pleat, my green petticoat disappears. Only cheap women wear fabric thin enough to let it show.

Beauty. Comb your hair every morning. Use only one handful of your Eid oil; you know Memshahib hates the smell. Make your kajol line very thin; you are not Sri Devi; the only men that will pay attention to you are like Hakim from next door, with two wives in every district. Take a bath before lunch so that the others don't have to smell your stink. Use mendhi only for special days such as Eid and at weddings. Eat more rice, what husband will want your skinny bones? Remember to use neem twigs to clean your teeth. Stay out of the afternoon sun; if you sit chatting with Alam in the garden, you will become ugly as a dog.

The fourth I have to do carefully. If I have been doing things right, there should be a hole in front of my right leg, and I must make certain it will be hidden under the next fold.

Hospitality. When Rohima Aunty's children come with their ayah, make sure she gets tea and nashta before leaving. It does not look good to let her leave on an empty stomach. They talk about these things afterwards. Also if you see that a driver has been waiting for more than an hour, get him some too. But when you go to him, remember to cover your head and do not look him in the face if you can avoid it, you being such a hussy. If Apa wants paan and there is none in the kitchen, give her yours; the poor girl has to listen to Memshahib screaming all day as it is. When home on your day off, if anybody visits, be the first one to seat them and cook for them. Show everybody that you're not like your lazy cousin Sokena.

After the fifth, without fail, I worry that I have been too generous with the pleats and that there will not be enough at the end. Even though I checked with the fourth.

Modesty. Always cover your head with your sari. So what if Alam Bhai is like a father? A harlot like you is always scheming. Dry your petticoat and undergarments inside, it will take longer but we don't want to embarrass others with your filth. Sit with your legs tucked underneath. Do not use the wooden stool if there are any men around, use a clean piece of the floor. Learn to speak quieter; nobody wants to hear a woman's whine. Speak little to anyone that is not close family; never tell too much, only what you must. If there is new darwan in the house, make sure to tie your hair before leaving your room. This is the right way to cut cloth for a blouse. This is how you cover your head when you hear the Azan. Always remember or else your son will not grow up a good Muslim.

With the last fold, I am ready to start the day. I throw the end over my left shoulder and tuck it in at the front. Hopefully, it will last till my afternoon bath, after which I will start all over again with my other sari.

So we can hear the cacophony that was Babu, the manifold voices that he saturated. I can only wonder how he managed to keep his sanity and hold on to himself, to the ground below. Maybe he heard too much; maybe that is why he gave up on us. Or didn't he? That is a question only he could answer.

ASHLEY FAULKNER

Striving for Emotion

Ashley Faulkner was born in 1977 and comes from Lisburn, Northern Ireland. He graduated with a BA in English Literature from Queens' University Belfast and won the Esther Ballantine prize for that subject. He is currently compiling his first collection of poetry.

The Maternal Code

By the time she arrived home it had stopped crying.
She found the blue lips a little comical. No redness
returned, even when she applied a damp dishcloth.
She stuck a finger down its throat and felt no breath,
or saliva. The tongue seemed almost hard. Lighting
a cigarette she smoked a while, thoughtfully, careful
that no ash flicked on its skin. Then she unstrapped
it from the pushchair, pressed a fist against its chest,
ruled out suffocation. She set it on the floor, looked up.
The frost had turned the window into fractured ice.
She liked winter. Smiling, she took off her thick coat,
made herself a hot drink, rubbed warmth into her hands.

august 22nd

The first news bulletin brought fear from you,
thankfully alleviated: a bomb, several injured.
Saturday afternoon should have been massacre.
We made food, waiting for the next update –
gameshows dulling our defences, softening
our minds to passing salt, the cat's whereabouts.
Then, while you cut a slice of meat: twenty-one
dead, more than a hundred estimated injured,
five seconds of fact releasing your fork: "God no."
Hurrying to the phone, calling sister, brother,
leaving me to predict the ones split unstitchable.

The Summer Christ Died

She told me that Satan hid behind the raspberry canes,
danced the roofs, gazed down from the vast blue skies.
In thinking of Him I would be condemned to hellfire.
In not thinking of Him I left my soul open to corruption.
At six years, I wanted to make treehouses, while she
quoted messages from Revelations with a seven year zeal.

The next morning her father forced me into a corner,
demanding whether she had trampled the raspberry canes.
I could not lie when the Devil was within and outside of me.
That afternoon she was late: limping, full of astonishment
at the Judas act I had performed. In her eyes I saw the fear
of that horsewhip, brandished by the darkest Lord she knew.

Reducing the Clans

That afternoon was spent dealing blow after blow
with a stick he had crafted into a club, until
the action felt dull to his senses and the manner
in which they crumpled, tried to rise, reminded him
of fish slithering to water that did not exist.

By evening his club split, and he finished the last one
with his knuckles, wincing at the pain from his wrist.
He was tired, yet his task was not done. Lifting
a spade, he looked up at the dusk sky, then started
to dig earth where no outstretched arm got in the way.

Decision Made

Standing there with a tight-buttoned coat,
bright yellow stripes, foldable white stick,
he asked me if this was the bus to the airport.
I wanted to reply, but wasn't entirely sure
whether I should answer to his eyes
or look down at his feet with an apt dignity.

My hesitation made him stare at me –
and I stared back, to check his focus.
The irises were milky blue, the pupils flitted:
I bowed my head, mumbled, "Yes. You've
found the right place." Unfolding his stick,
he began to talk of the congestion of the town,

expecting a response. I gazed over his shoulder
and agreed, hoping that he might notice
the detachment in my voice. With a brief nod
of thanks, he aimed his stick for the ground
and launched forward, glancing left and right,
as if from doubt or certainty, or simple parody.

Botanic/Stranmillis

(i)

Peace, Belfast, your blood-infamous streets
too close at heart for me to write any more.
A local voice might have slowed the spate
of verse not introduced to your delicacies:
the street-turns, the hatred splinters, the sky.
Even the mention of you conjures a friend
vulnerable to gossip, cracked ribs and stooped.
I will hold you level, but never elevate you far.

(ii)

I walked those streets yesterday afternoon
for the first time in eight weeks, mingled
with the shoppers and settled to the dialect.
The winter skies were huge and motionless,
creating a mood of contentment in identity.
Newspaper stands bore the same events,
re-enacted until their drama seemed secondary
to the buying of presents, the holding of hands.
If I had looked up and closed my eyes, I could
have convinced myself anywhere, unassaulted.

Reaching for the Verge

We breaked for nectarines and I saw her:
lying, one leg curled, one arm flung out
as if to catch the groceries rolling to a halt
across the three lanes without an over-bridge.
Those huge eyes collecting drizzle, gazing
at the clutch of her fingers where the nails
had been shredded and red funnelled knuckles;
I too could not blink. From the grotesque yawn
of metal beside her, milk cartons and meat
flopped into engine fluid, spattered the soft
floral print of her dress, the billows of which
were not to settle as we drove north for home.

From the Bough

He wanted to jump, having climbed further
than ever before, hands reaching out for slim
branches, feet digging into bark, until he clung
to the trunk and drew breath. But they had not
emerged from indoors, and they needed to see.
Clasping tighter, shuffling feet, he looked up
and grimaced, hissed out their names, furious
that they were delaying, when they knew. Then
their voices, anxious, panicking, beneath him.
He glanced down: father, hugging arms, mother
urging him to descend, carefully, inch by inch.
His fingers were loosening. Stunned noises escaped
from father – he twisted his neck, until he gazed
into those eyes, and there was understanding. The
release was effortless, even elegant, as rushing
air brought the lunge of father near, nearest to him.

Preparations before Retiring

It was after eleven, she had changed into night-clothes,
checked that the front door was locked; now she moved
for the kitchen, closed her eyes. She wanted sleep, exhausted
by three long days of work. Building up determination,
she opened her eyes and strode that tireless circumference,
studying electrical goods as she went: the microwave,
unplugged; the oven, no red display; the toaster, disconnected;
the kettle, cord bundled, safe. She switched off the lights
and hurried for the hallway, already thinking of taking
the staircase, easing under blankets; but her feet backtracked,
her hand raised to switch on the light; she was making sure
that the microwave was disconnected, the toaster unplugged,
the tap did not drip. This done, she switched off the lights,
yet she was wavering, wanting to test the oven for warmth,
the kettle for steam–she had already reached the microwave,
fingers tracing the plug points. Her body shivering, whines
building in her throat, she looked out at the darkness, aware
that soon dawn would arrive, with all sockets charred black.

From Rachel

She sat down at the table and wrote to daddy
who was seven years dead, pleading with him
to return from his holiday and order mummy
to care for her again, to throw out that man
who could not love, as daddy had done. Laughter
never came from the kitchen now, just silence
when she entered, mummy looking shocked
and that man moving away, tucking in his shirt, as if
he was guilty of something, then glaring at her,
telling her to get out when she only wanted to talk,
speak to mummy about her worries. She knew daddy
still thought of her from his sun-lounger, cold drink
in one hand and hot sand in the other, enjoying
the paddle of his toes in clear water. If only he
could get a flight and come home with presents
in both arms and not smell the way he did, dressed –
up in the coffin while mummy sprayed perfume
so that uncles and aunties did not think badly of him.

KAREN GOODWIN

Wearing the Stones

Karen Goodwin was born in Swansea, 1976. She studied at the University of Wales, Aberystwyth, and is currently working on her first collection of poems.

Out of Water

My mother is wild.
When she brushes her hair

it flames in a halo of snakes.
Unfettered, black wisps

merge, then separate.
She has come from the tropics –

a pink fish, electric
in movement – her spine

twists from its centre
to rage in all directions.

Ballet

Every Saturday, hair scraped and stabbed
with pins, temples throbbing
to the iron piano, ankles
bound in neat, pink silk,

the door opened on our bodies
to become less. Slighter than feathers,
transformed to a cat's step, papery hands
held, while the untrained breath

shuddered in our bones,
as if one birth were not enough.
We pushed and locked our hips,
grew tall with invisible string,

but time brought on breasts;
shadows on the mirrored walls.
And I foresaw a future of being less
in order to balance on my toes.

The Manuscript

A pool of red ink
stills to its surface;
words yet to be salvaged
beneath the mouth of a tin pail.

Urine peppers his fingers,
the scent of ritual –
as he dips and lifts his quill
puts point to new stretched skin.

"Every word written
makes the devil writhe in agony;"
he curls his first stroke,
copies from skin to skin.

Slowly, the day becomes pure.

Niobe with Flowers

Inhaling,
the wide skirts of her tent-dress
billow like giant lungs;
launching and setting themselves
against a backdrop of bricked up sky,
she blooms, bulbous and red,
poised in remembrance.

"Has it happened yet?"
The lights hum with electric sterility,
a flurry of doctors pass and leave
their laughter to soundless corridors.
Alone,
she weeps alone,
for there are no ceremonies,
the stiff white surgeon with hands to extract
seals a brief transaction.

The June sun warms the tongues of stone
to green, then follows the bloom –
fourteen sepal heads push through
a glossy wax foetus.
In ritual secrecy her tears
animate the children she cannot bear;
nourishing the squinting pinks, azures,
until, plunging like parachutes,
the flowers expand and die.

Branwen's Letter

Carried in the scale of birdsong
over the sea, her words, vibrations
rattled in the giant pod of his ear.

He interpreted the message –
saw his sister's face reflected
in the eye of the bird, its jet glass

held her steady, flickered
and was gone. Yet its detail
of imprisonment stayed in his vision,

until he rose to make thunders
break from his boot, funnelled a path
turned on either side of his weight,

across the waters to reach her.
Some thought him a mountain
moved miraculously to the shore, his eyes

two lakes born from the sea's hollow.
But she knew it was her brother
come to return her, it had been foretold;

how the sky would crack in his fury,
and the country would never see such bloodshed.

Wolf

First sight of the Pyrenees –
nothing but us and the car's spotlight
pushed out before us like cold antennae.

Your hand at the wheel gauged our way
through darkness, kept to the inside wall
of rock, our only compass from the edge.

Rain began to clip the roof, its thin pulse
thickened on windows, drummed its hooves
into a storm, drawing us in at each bend.

And then, the sky lit up, white and feverish
the electric trees and the figure of a wolf
flashed across our path, made us swerve,

look back. I was terrified, an omen I was sure,
holding a great blank for our future,
the white heat of a sky doubled in its stomach.

That night, as I lay in your arms, I listened
for the howl of cold through your veins,
glimpsed the marble streak behind your eyes.

Sunrise

My bike treads quietly in the sleeping streets,
rolls to a stop, leans at the base of a switched off
lamp-post. Seventy-six, the cat with one eye
punctured, mews for its eye's lost button,
watches me cross lawns, disappear behind hedges.

The first trees lighten, telephone wires
strung taught, tingle in anticipation of the day,
the horizon comes clear over an outcrop of houses.
As I traipse out my morning, the moon
fades like a worn coin, changes place with the sun.

TIM GUEST

from *Gravity's angels*

Despite many people's belief that it's just a chat-up line, Tim Guest really did grow up in a commune. *Gravity's angels* is a memoir of his childhood as a disciple of the Indian guru Bhagwan Shree Rajneesh, in England, India and Oregon, USA. Beginning with his birth in 1975, it charts his time in the commune until the movement erupted in Oregon in 1986, and the subsequent struggle to rediscover family life.

I.
"Buddham Sharanam Gachchami"
(I bow to the feet of the Awakened One)
- first of the three vows of Gautama the Buddha

Taking Sannyas

I have a group photo of the commune. About forty people are gathered together on the lawn in front of a huge manor house. You can spot a woman to the left of centre, near the front, in black and white. She's standing square on, with one hip jutting out, and her arms are folded in a habitual attempt to disrupt restrictive bourgeois conditioning and the sexist division of labour. My mother. She is twenty-nine years old, with a thin, pretty face and long twig-like limbs. The wiry hair she used to iron as a girl has finally been allowed to spring into a bush about her head. She's standing with the other shot-callers of the commune – Adheera, Poonam, Weechee – all women, all with their arms crossed, and all in charge.

I remember the moment when our journey towards that photo began. I was three years old. My mother was sitting in our living room, with the lights low and the electric fire on. I watched her drain the last of her wine and put the glass onto the coffee table, where a cassette case lay on its side. She flipped the case over in her hands. Wrapping her thick dressing gown around her legs, she read out the name on the back cover: "Bhagwan Shree Rajneesh". Bhagwan looked out from the front with wide shining eyes. I had seen the tape-cover earlier in the day and laughed; even then I was startled by the look in his eyes. In every photo I have seen since, Bhagwan has always worn that same expression: a wide-eyed mix of craziness and wonder. The photo on the tape cover was blurred so you couldn't make out any individual strands of hair, and this made his long white beard look like a spray of mist around his smooth brown face. Above his photo, the title of the cassette was emblazoned on a star-field background in laser-reds and purples: 'Beyond the Frontiers of the Mind'.

She tilted her head and listened. I was lying in front of the fire scribbling with felt-tips in a colouring book. Apart from the scratching of my pens against paper, the house was silent. After a moment she leaned forward to put the tape into the machine, and sat back. She took a long drag of a joint resting in an ashtray on the arm of the sofa. Smoke folded over her head as the crackle of the tape became Bhagwan's voice. "If you look at the small child… even a just-born baby…" His deep voice seemed to purr and crawl towards me by the fire like our cat Tabitha padding her way across the carpet. "…you can see he has started groping for something; his hands are trying to find out something." *Some-tinghhh…* He drew out the last sound of every sentence into a hiss. "The child has started the journey. In the journey he will lose himself…"

I awoke when the tape came to the end of the second side – click, click, click. My mother sat still. Her cheeks glinted red and orange. She pulled up the corner of her dressing gown, then wiped it across her face where she was wet with tears.

Eventually, although she was afraid, my mother sent a letter to Bhagwan. "Several weeks ago," she wrote, "I listened to a tape of you speaking. I felt you were speaking to a part of me that has never been spoken to before. I have heard that the way to learn from you is to become a 'sannyasin', one of your followers. I would therefore like to take sannyas from you and go deeply into all that this may mean." What she didn't write, what I knew, was that she had cried every day since hearing his voice. What she told no one was that she could still hear him. Over and over in her head, his voice was still saying: "You have come home." (*You haf cum-homhhh…*)

We can't see my mother's colours in the photograph, but I'll fill them in: her face is pale pink; fawn freckles spatter her face and arms like big raindrops; the hair that spirals out from under her peasant shawl is a bright and startling red. She does have something of the peasant in her; she's a stock-in-trade working-class girl, the eldest daughter of Roman Catholic parents. Her own mother was the daughter of a poor Irish family, in which only three out of ten children survived. My grandmother was the seventh daughter of a seventh daughter, and descended from Irish kings – or so she said. She would corner my mother in their house and tell her that because of this magical lineage she was a witch and could tell everything that my mother was thinking. And, she muttered, she didn't like it one bit.

As a child my mother would place toy blocks under her bedclothes to mortify her flesh. She had always been thought of as holy and was considering becoming a Carmelite nun – a mendicant order, enclosed and often silent. In her morning prayers one Sunday she asked God for a sign. At church that day, she opened up her prayer book and a holy picture fell out. On the back was a prayer from St Theresa of Lisieux, a Carmelite nun: *'I desire to reserve nothing for myself but freely and most willingly to sacrifice myself and all that is mine to thee.'*

"Uncanny," I said when she told me this recently, "that's you." Because it is: it's the story of her life.

"Yes. Exactly," she said. "Although not any more," she added, "I'm getting better."

In her late teens, and to the great loss of nuns the world over, my mother discovered other things: sex, guilt, drugs, politics, more guilt. When you look closely at the sparkle in her eyes, even from the wide angle of this group photo, you can catch a glint of something manic in the brightness. With nowhere to go, no escape from the crushing weight of her worry and guilt and the deeply-planted doctrines of the Catholic Church, my mother pushed herself up and out, creating a new her – available, willing, bright-eyed and sincere – and a new world for this new her to inhabit, in which everything was – in a loud, high, lilting voice – "perfectly fine!" She painted her old self out of the picture so well that it sometimes surprises me that she could be captured on film at all.

My mother was keen to help reclaim childbirth from the hands of doctors and back into the hands of women – "Our Bodies, Our Selves!" she would chant when required – so she gave birth to me at home. Two hours into labour, on the cusp of transition – the point at which the woman's body takes over the birth process completely – my mother stopped gasping and turned to the midwife. "Okay, that's it," she said. "Stop. I've changed my mind. You can all go home now. It's fine." Then her neck lolled back, and the wet dome of my head began to emerge from between her legs. As I came out, the midwife could see that the umbilical cord was wrapped around my neck – "You went dancing too much, love, while you were pregnant," she told my mother afterwards. As quickly as I was being born, I was being strangled. Because the cord was wrapped around twice, the midwife couldn't unhook it, so she took up a pair of scissors and cut the cord while I was still being born. "Your oxygen supply was cut too soon," my mother told me recently. "You can blame all your problems on that, if you like."

There are black and white photos of the birth, exact records of the light which fell on us the moment I arrived. They were used to illustrate an article in *Spare Rib*, a feminist monthly. Called 'In the beginning', the piece is a favourable look at home birth, "with a loving father or husband and perhaps even a granny on hand". My mother is pictured on the bottom right hand corner, lying on our living room floor with her legs spread apart, holding me in both arms. My face is scrunched and bawling, hers is open and wet with sweat. We, the blankets, and the mattress, are all covered in a dark grey that looks like it should be blood, but my mother assures me is just water and shadow. The photos are credited to John, my father. He told me years later how it felt to be there at the birth of your son: "The thing is, you know, there's two of you, and you go into this room. Then there's a lot of blood and shouting, and all of a sudden, you know, there's three of you."

There is a set of about a hundred passport photos that were taken once a week for nearly two years after my birth. At first we're pictured together – my mother and John and me all crowded into the booth, perched on the small swivel stool. In the first few photos my mother is looking down at me. I am asleep and oblivious to her smile. Further down the page, I have opened my eyes and grown some hair and my mother's gaze has moved up to meet the single eye of the camera. A few pages on she begins to look up and off to the left, with wide, vacant eyes and a rapturous smile. These photos show a much greater likeness of my father than the photo from the commune. He looks more relaxed here, more down to earth than my mother; his huge sideburns don't seem to care whether they meet or lazily miss his untamed Zapata moustache. In some of the photos his eyes are nearly closed.

Later that year my mother and father split up and it was John who continued taking me to the booth. In the first of the photos in which only he and I are present, John looks utterly different; if I didn't know any better, I'd swear he has fobbed me off with a look-alike friend. He's giving the camera a plucky stare, his head tilted up to display his Adam's apple, daring us to recognise him, but his face is the wrong shape – too long – and his makeshift stubble is a poor substitute for John's elaborate moustache. I am gazing down into the corner, looking appropriately short-changed. In the next picture the familiar John is back, but only just; his moustache has grown beyond all reason and he wears a distrustful squint. He has joined a Cuba Libra movement since we were last at the booth and is holding me up to the camera for a ransom photo. Or so it seems. I look my part, slumped with his hands in my armpits, staring down at the floor in a nylon jump-suit, my hair hanging in thick curls over my eyes. It's not just him that changes with each photo. In one of the last ones, it looks like he has brought someone else's child – a girl, dressed as a sailor – into the booth by mistake. In all of them he meets the gaze of the camera with a grin and holds me carefully on his right knee.

From as early as I can remember, John and my mother lived separately. John would come to my mother's house on Saturday morning, chat with her over a cup of tea, then take me over to his house. He lived in a flat above a nursery in the Chapeltown area of Leeds and, for the rest of the weekend, I would run around with the kids in the playground. All

Saturday night the bass from the reggae dancehall behind the nursery shook the floor and rattled the window frames. On Monday John would cycle to work at Leeds Polytechnic with me on a little blue seat above the back wheel. I would point to people and trees and cars and buildings with my mittens, mouth open, curly blond hair blowing in the wind, trying to tell him about the things I could see but the wind filled my mouth and emptied my lungs. I spent the days falling off the climbing frame in the Polytechnic nursery. In the afternoon we would walk back along the river, him pushing the bicycle with one hand on the saddle. He would steer it somehow although he never touched the handlebars.

It was on the nursery climbing frame that I lost my first teeth. My mother had gone to India to see Bhagwan – she had thrown her Chinese coins with holes in the middle on the kitchen table and come back out into the living room with the Book of Changes held open with her thumb. "Ch'ien – the way of Heaven," she said. Her eyes rolled along the line. "The character of Heaven in all its perfection." She turned the page, raising her hand like an actor declaiming on the stage. "Dragon appearing in the field. It furthers one to see the great man." She flicked on a few pages.

"There is no game in the field," she added, "go now."

So she did. And, as the months passed and she didn't return, I decided to take refuge in gravity. It took me three falls from the climbing frame and two sets of stitches before I finally managed to knock out my three front teeth, and an obliging photographer took a picture of me at a charity fair in the local church. The photo appeared in the *Leeds Evening Post*. In it, my tongue pokes through the gaps in my teeth like sunlight through vandalised stained glass. I'm wearing a woollen sweater with zig-zag bands across the middle. My trousers are hanging low on my waist; I'd be holding them up if the balloon – tied to the end of a long piece of string that snakes up above me from my fist – didn't have my full attention. It looks as if it might be me keeping the balloon aloft, but I know that it was filled with helium and required no effort at all. At the top of the picture is the newspaper's caption: 'Dreams take flight'.

My father cut it out and sent it to my mother, and two weeks later she came home. We met her at the airport. "I met Bhagwan," she told my father. "He told me I should help set up the British Buddhafield. My energy's right for it. You know?"

"Far out," he said.

John was never at the commune for more than a few months at a time, so his presence in the group photo is unusual. He is standing at the front, near the side, with an easy exit out the frame. The only feature you can see clearly from this distance is his long, thick moustache, with droopy ends like the boughs on a willow tree. It looks as if he may have planted it there so that his mouth could seek shelter under it when the weather turned bad. He is like that, my father; his shelter is himself.

It is only because of John that these photos and cuttings still exist. My mother has since burned or lost or discarded everything she had back then. There are many other photos in the folders John has kept for all these years, but it's the group photograph from the commune that I keep returning to, because it's the only one in which the four of us – me, my mother, my father, my step-father – are all pictured together.

Near the back, squatting on a log, to the right of the frame but closer to the centre than my father, is the man who was to become my step-father. A vest exposes his broad shoulders, and his legs – provocatively, raucously splayed – are confined above the knee in the shorts of an English schoolboy. His face crawls with wild-man hair and his cheeks look dark, as if they might still bear remnants of rouge from a cabaret the night before. He is smiling an ingratiating, almost guilty smile – but it is a helpless guilt. His smile tells us that whatever he has done, he will do again, in spite of us and in spite of himself. You might have seen him on his way to India in a bus, in Iran or Afghanistan, had you been there in the mid-seventies – met him at a campsite, or broken down by the side of the road, or hitched a lift. You might have greeted him: "Have you finished with the West yet?" "Yes, I've finished with the West." If so, you would have seen his shorts and his guilty smile and perhaps thought this: that long ago he had run out of the school grounds at lunch-time, discovered life in the woods, and never come home.

The day my mother sent her letter to Bhagwan, a sannyasin arrived on her doorstep. He invited her out to a party where she watched two men dressed in orange clear the dance-floor with an improvised performance, to the applause of the whole crowd. The climax of the dance was a dog-walk, in which one man – the owner – and the other man – the dog – took turns to walk each other. The man playing the dog was called Suranjana. My mother was captivated.

There is a dance where the dancers whirl into the centre, and do not re-emerge. This was the dance the sannyasins were trying to perfect, and they soon started trying to perfect it in our living room. To most people – including my best friend Georgie's mother – sannyasins were known as 'the Orange People', and after my mother took sannyas, everyone who came to sit around in that living room wore orange: orange dungarees, orange draw-string trousers, orange robes, orange sandals. My mother dyed all her clothes in the bath – to my delight, they left permanent orange stains on the fireguard – and they began holding 'meetings' in our living room, from some of which I was carefully excluded.

As I understand it now, the purpose of these meetings was spiritual transcendence. They were attempts to learn, through direct experience – the Tantric way – about those human agonies that bind us to the earth: need, fear, jealousy, the desire for power and self-gratification. These were spiritual obstacles that had to be learned about directly in order to be overcome. For sannyasins, direct experience transcended history and truth was a disco lyric – "Life is Life!"

"The energy is here right now," they'd say to each other in the meetings. "This is the time to begin." So they did. They fought a lot and had sex with each other. At the time, all I noticed were one or two new stains on the living room walls.

The first time Suranjana came to my attention as distinct from all the other bearded men, was one morning a few weeks after the meetings began. I woke up to find the sun already in my room. Bright specks drifted in the line of light that slanted between my curtain and the floor. I wondered whether the sparks had always been there and woke up like me, with the arrival of the light, or whether they had ridden on the light all the way from the sun. I thought that my mum would know. I got out of bed and walked across the room in my pyjamas, rubbing sleepy-dust from my eyes. Brilliant flecks whirled around me. I walked to the shelves and picked up my favourite toy – a big red metal fire engine with a moving ladder – and held it against my hip, reaching up with my other hand to turn the doorknob. Downstairs, I turned the handle to my mother's room and tiptoed in. A crack of sunlight slipped in with me and leant against the far wall. Sparks flooded in across the bed. Pulling back the covers, I pushed myself up and found my face in a mess of thick, black hair. I slid back down. My mother's hair was red. This hair was black. Walking round to the top of the bed, I reached forward and pulled at the hair, standing on my tiptoes to look at the other side of the head. It was a man. The front of his head was as black and hairy as the back. Around his neck was a string of beads – dark brown wooden beads with lines on them like cut wood, that ran down over his chest and under the covers. He groaned and shifted his arm from underneath him. I let go of his hair, dropping his head back onto the pillow. He lay still. I held my fire engine out above him and began to bang it against his head.

On my birthday that year, Suranjana made me a huge cake in the shape of a castle. It had blue icing for stone ramparts, with chocolate buttons as holes for Lego men to shoot arrows through, and a huge black liquorice gate. I hoped he would stay for my next birthday because he made the best cakes I had ever seen.

I am in the commune photo too. I'm on the concrete porch at the back, out to the left side, sprawled over a beanbag. I'm holding a book out in front of me at a determined angle; I have already been here for three years, but I'm still doing my best to keep the world at bay. I am wearing a smaller version of the wooden bead necklace that is worn by all the adults around me. Although the photo is black and white, I can tell you that the clothes I am wearing – the shrunken T-shirt (with 'You Are The March Event!' splashed across the front), the baggy draw-string trousers, the corduroy waistcoat lined with sheepskin – have all been dyed various colours of the sunrise, either on purpose or because they have been washed time and time again in the communal laundries. The sun has brought the freckles out on my face. Tangled hair billows about my head. I look like a tawny angel.

II.

"Sangham Sharanam Gachchami"
(I bow to the feet of the commune of the Awakened One)
- *second of the three vows of Gautama the Buddha*

The British Buddhafield

My mother was interviewed for the *Rajneesh Buddhafield European Newsletter* in June 1981, two years after she took sannyas, and six months before The British Buddhafield was to open. "For over ten years I've been trying to create or be part of something like this," she says, "a society that's based on something other than politics. I've tried it in countless different forms: feminist communities, collectives, therapy communes – but none of them worked. This one does – because of Bhagwan." When she first heard a tape of Bhagwan, she says, "I broke down and saw all my fear and how I was always trying to understand life – and that I didn't really know what it was about. It was very hard for a while. I couldn't talk to any of my friends; they were all political, 'mindy', and for the first time I had no intellectual justification for what I was doing and feeling. I came to realise that you can't change the structures of society without changing yourself." She grins out from the black and white photo next to the interview, wearing a woollen polo-neck sweater that must be orange. A shy smile stretches out under the explosive bush of her hair, like she's just been teased. "Sannyasins are such an amazing people; the fact that we cover such a wide spectrum gives us so much richness. We have so much to give to the world."

The British Buddhafield turned out to be Herringswell Manor, an Edwardian manor house with five large out-houses, in fourteen acres of Suffolk countryside. The British Buddhafield. Never in history have so many full-facial beards and so many Indian names pronounced in English and American accents gathered together in the heart of the Suffolk countryside, to wear so much maroon. Bhagwan Shree Rajneesh gave a name to it: 'Medina Rajneesh, Neo-Sannyas Commune'. Medina Rajneesh was a place where children could be free from the oppression of parents, and parents could be free from the oppression of kids. On the lawn in front of the Main House at Medina was where the group photograph was taken. In Medina, even the signs in the toilets loved you:

'Beloved, please wash your hands. Love, ♥'.

In every photo from Medina, my mother stands amidst the big-time players of English sannyas. The big-shots, the hustlers of Bhagwan, were mostly women, and all therapists; my mother was no exception. She worked in the Medina Rajneesh therapy and health centre, Hadiqua'a – Sanskrit for 'The Walled Garden of Truth'. She held individual therapy sessions and ran groups with names like 'Absolute Freedom', 'Acceptance', 'Insight and Awareness' and 'Motherhood'. Apart from some evenings when she sneaked off work (which was called 'Worship') for twenty minutes to visit me at bedtime, Hadiqua'a was the only place I would see her. I would run down across the daisy field, mala flailing, carrying a piece of paper folded with flaps arranged so I could move it around in my fingers to reveal the writing under each flap. I would bang on the door of her room until she let me in, then wave the paper in her face, folding and unfolding the flaps and chanting "One, two, three, four, I fancy Tarangita," (or, depending on which week it was, Purva, or Deepa, or Soma), "One, two, three, four…" Behind me, Swami Deva Prabhodam (or something similar – Swabodhi, say, or Nikhilananda) would be 'freaking out' because Ma Mukta (or Veetmoha, or Chaitanya Keerti) had left him for Swami Prem Purvodaya (or Garimo, or

Bodhisattva). He would pause mid-whoop, fists poised above a weary cushion, and glare at me until I left. People complained and I was discouraged from visiting her at Worship. It got so that I rarely saw her, except in passing.

One evening I was sitting in an armchair in a bay window in the Main House, watching some of the other kids play on the grass outside, when I heard my mother laugh. I could see the room behind me reflected in the glass: I watched her enter with Kirti, an old Indian man we had met at the Ashram in Poona. They sat down at a coffee table, sipping tea and chatting. The sky grew darker. Outside, the kids continued to play their game.

"Tell me about my love-life, Kirti," my mother said. In the reflection on the window, Kirti had picked up my mother's wrist and was tracing her hand with his long, thin fingers.

"You don't want me to tell you about your spiritual path?" he said. (*Spiridual Pardh?* was what I heard.) My mother laughed.

"No. Tell me about my love-life." Chinmaya emerged from the wooden hut on the edge of the path by the lawn, wearing his woollen hat. I watched him chop logs in the half-light, swinging the axe high above a thick stump, one after the other, splitting them with a single swing each time.

"By the way, Vismaya," Kirti said, (*by dee weh, Vish-may-a,*) "Do you know what your name is meaning?"

"Bhagwan told me," my mother said, half laughing. "It means 'Wonder' in Sanskrit."

"Heh-eh-eh-egh." Kirti laughed at this and coughed, his eyes shining, his hands flapping palm-upwards on his knees. "No no, no no."

"What do you mean?" she asked.

"Say to me your name," Kirti said.

"Kirti," my mother said. Her tone was admonishing. "You know my name."

"Yes, I know your name. Say it to me how you are saying it."

My mother spoke her name: "Vismaya." (*Viz-ma-ya.*) Kirti laughed again. "What? Come on Kirti." She was enjoying being teased.

Kirti sighed. "Saying it like this, *Vish-may-a*, it means

'Wonder', yes, you are right in thinking." (*Dright in tinking.*) "Saying it this way you are saying it, *Viz-ma-ya*, it is not meaning 'Wonder', oh no."

"What *does* it mean?" My mother asked.

"Viz-ma-ya?" In the reflection, I could see Kirti looking straight at her. "'Viz' in Sanskrit is meaning 'Poison', from the teeth of the cobra snake. 'Maya' is meaning 'Illusion'. Your name, when you are saying it, is meaning 'Poisonous Illusion'." Kirti laughed softly, "Egh-heh-egh-hegh," and in the darkening window, children scattered across the reflection of my mother's face.

PRAVEEN HERAT

from *A Theory of Everything*

Praveen Herat was born in South London in 1976, of Sri Lankan descent, and educated at Dulwich College, London, and St. John's College, Oxford. *A Theory of Everything* is his first work, a 'polyphonic' novel about grief, prejudice and illusory love. The novel consists of four different narratives which combine, clash and harmonise around these themes; not unlike the instruments in a string quartet. What follows is the novel's opening movement.

1

–One more question. You're in a white room. You're naked. How do you feel? In three adjectives.

–What do you mean, 'a white room'?

–Exactly that. A room with white walls. White everything. Just whiteness. Look, Billie, it's perfectly simple. Just tell us how you feel.

She could feel herself blushing, her heart beating faster, her chest contracting python-tight. The sunlight stitched itself in the windowpane and needled her eyes.

–But you'll explain it to me. You won't laugh. You'll tell me what it means.

They laughed all the more in their high, tine-bright voices. But she didn't notice them now. She was captivated by the white room. She imagined a square formed by white-washed walls with wooden floors like those of a gallery space. In the centre of the room was a plinth – a cuboid white as albumen across which she was draped naked and supine. She had the sensation of her arms dangling over its sides as if the threads holding her up had suddenly been snipped away.

–Well. How do you feel?

She couldn't answer instantly. She felt abandonment, guilt. She felt sacrificed.

–Contemplative... Unsettled... Accepting... I think? Why do you look so serious? Was that not right?

–No, not at all...

–Look – she felt she had to run, do anything to get herself out of that room – I've got to go. You can tell me what it means another time. I've got to go.

The closing door soft-pedalled the voices calling after her.

She didn't want the key to their tame quiz anyway. Let them laugh – to tell the truth she had wanted them to laugh. Being the object of laughter was being different.

Out in the street, with the adrenalin coursing along her temples, she ran aimlessly through the labyrinth of terraced houses, and then she stopped, and then she ran again. The exhilaration of escape made her see everything for the first time: the sinking sun smoothing the cornices, warming the redbrick; shimmering in the distance, in one-point perspective, the ilex and maple in the parkfields flashing flamelike green and gold. And when she stopped running and took possession of herself again, she was thankful their laughter had given her this awareness. They could never possess it. It was like Remembrance Day at school, standing very still for the minute's silence out at the memorial: the birdsong, the wind chasing across the landscape, this sense of gratefulness for suffering.

What the fuck. It couldn't take much to figure out the meaning of their little games. Tests like that always dealt with taboos, so the white room could only be sex or death. And so what if she was thinking of him, of her father. Five letters. Anagram of hated. Heat and eat within it. Head. Hate. Had. He.

The.

A.

Yes. It was right that the words we use to designate anything – definite and indefinite articles – were part of its word stock.

2

There are twelve people. Six of them are men and six of them are women. They are twelve good men and true. They are sitting in the white room around a wooden table.

The clock is running half an hour fast.

One of the men stands up.

"This clock is running half an hour fast," he says. He walks over to it, reaches up, groans, unhooks it and adjusts his paunch.

He looks at the back of the clock. "There's no knob to adjust it," he says.

Another man says, "There must be a way of changing the time." He is wearing shorts. His legs are pale.

"No. Nothing at all," says the man with the paunch.

"Can't be," says the know-all in shorts. He leans back in his chair and puts his hands behind his head.

"I said there's no knob, nothing."

Paunch reaches up, groans, rehooks it and adjusts his paunch. He wipes the sweat from his brow. His face is very red. Know-All and Paunch watch the clock tick on in its own time zone.

"I'm sure there's a way," says Know-All under his breath.

They fall silent. A young Asian man says, "Even a stopped clock tells the right time twice a day."

"It's not stopped. It's just fast," says Know-All. He smoothes his moustache with the thumb and forefinger of his right hand.

The twelve people in the white room do not have names. It is their unanimous verdict that they are not going to tell each other their names. Occasionally they all begin to talk at once for a few seconds. Then they fall into silence and stare at the floor under the table.

In the silence one of the men stands up, sighs and walks over to the broad window. He looks out across the view of the city. There are many tower blocks, a suspension bridge, a dome, a clock-tower. The clock in the clocktower is not working. He sees that the clock is not working and smiles.

The door opens. A man dressed in a a black gown walks in.

"If you'd like to follow me. We're ready for you now," he says.

SMILER stands at the window and watches the others file out. They are: KNOW-ALL; PAUNCH; ASIAN STUDENT; WORKING GIRL; GOTHIC GIRL; THE CLOWN; MAN-IN-SUIT; LITTLE OLD LADY; SILENT WOMAN; TIMID OLD MAN; CHRISTIAN WOMAN.

Smiler listens to them all as they walk out of the white room. He hears Gothic Girl say she is dying for a cigarette. He hears The Clown laugh to herself. He doesn't hear Paunch or Know-All.

Smiler sees Man-In-Suit hold the door open for the ladies. He sees Timid Old Man lean on his stick and shuffle towards the door. He watches Christian Woman hold his elbow and steer him through.

Smiler watches them all leaving, walks out and closes the door behind him.

The door opens again and Know-All walks into the empty white room. He walks up to the far wall, reaches up, unhooks the clock and stares at its plastic back.

"Well I'll be damned," he says.

3

What did it want from her anyway, this 'white room'? Questions kept bombarding her, like voices imploding on the school corridors at break. Why should an empty room be full of light – why hadn't she imagined the darkness of it? And if you existed in that room – if you found yourself there – did time exist? I mean, would you have a past, a beginning or an end? And what did you know?

A shape, a colour, a space – those things she knew – and the experience of those threads, the puppet threads, being snipped away, loose connections flapping from her limbs. Billie put her hands to her ears and massaged her temples but the voices wouldn't stop. She kept thinking of that woman in The Birds, arms up, beating the flashing flocks away from her breast. They came at her again, down the chimney into the boarded up house. Maybe it was the time you live in – the white room – and how you lived in it.

In the morning she had heard the voices in the shouts of the dustmen in the car park. She was going through the cuttings again, beating through the coarse coloured pages, and, with the salt-rime of sleep in her eyes, she had gone barefoot onto the walkway outside the flat, weighing the scrapbook in one hand and the rubbish chute door in the other. Down there, three storeys away, they were emptying the steel bins at the bottom of the chutes, bins taller than a man and half as much in diameter.

She remembered the tales her father would tell about them. Deep in the night – yes, it was true, quite, quite true – the witches used the bins as cauldrons to conjure their daemon menagerie. She could remember the roll-call: the man-eating Manticore – which can run faster than a bird can fly – with its lion pads, man-face and scorpion's sting; the bare-breasted bird-bodied Harpies – who watch over the souls of those who have committed violence against themselves; the flame-throwing Chimaera with its rabid maw, buck-fucking goat-body and serpent's flex; and its mother Echidna, yet another wild woman, a mythological mulatto part woman part snake.

They were devil-spawn, every one, but compound also: cross-caste – not unlike Billie herself and, for that, she felt kinship with them. Half-caste they used to say. Never a whole. Her father would offer roses in support. Hybrids, he would say, were actually a way to even greater beauty. Mixing kinds mended nature, was the art that nature makes. "You see, sweet maid, we marry a gentler scion to the wildest stock..." That was him all over, master of arcana, little-known plays, the byways never the highroad. When she had left school over the troubles – they spoke of it as if it was some political disaster! – he had taken over her education, and she had sat there for a year putting up with his ramblings, making him feel useful. Listening to the rantings also, at the end, in his very own white room. He had left her his piecemeal trivia, filled her with words you couldn't use when you were talking to people because they would think you were odd, or that you were supercilious, trying to show them up for all the things they didn't know. Standing on the balcony, weighing the door of the rubbish chute in one hand, holding the scrapbook aloft in the other, blinded by her biases towards him – all in all like some parody of Justice – standing there on the third floor balcony of a council flat that symbolised all his failings, she admitted that as far as life goes, he was a pundit and never the player he thought he was. But the view from that balcony, across London, was beautiful.

Her favourite daemon was no hybrid, though – it was the one with too many syllables, the Apis-thing, the beast he called Moby, the floating island beast. In stormy weathers unruly sailors would see its back basking in the waters, the colour of firm ground in roiling sea. Perhaps they cast anchor. Perhaps the grapnel lodged in Moby's scaly side. But he would not feel. And then they would take down the sails, disembark, unpack the tarred wineskins and drink libations to their gods – and their thoughts would turn to burnt offerings and the emptiness of their bellies. Soon they would have the fire going, scorching their thin strips of salted meat, lighting their bloodless faces in the oncoming dark. They would fall silent, gazing into its heart of light.

It was the fire that did it. Moby, unfazed by anchor prongs or the changings of the ocean, would know the fire. Its warmth seeps through him like blood in snow. And that is his signal to dive. The way her father told it you could imagine one perfect revolution. Dive, dive, leaving the sailors flailing in the black folds of ocean, and turn, turn Moby, swallow the splashing limbs, the skiff entire from stern to cracking bowsprit as you come round again, flesh and blood and oars and all.

These were the worlds within her father's bubbling vats, worlds of winged sphinxes, human-headed soul birds, unicorns, gorgons.

That year they found an ear in the bins – a severed human ear amongst the onion skins and chicken wings – and he didn't tell any more of his stories. Policemen formed a line across the width of the car park and made their way across it on their hands and knees, as if the chief constable had lost his contact lens and they were making a thorough search. Apisdochelone – that was the sea monster's name. Dochelone; lonely docks. Sailors' wives weeping at the end of the jetty. She could see their wetted lashes and chapped lips.

4

Outside the court the cameras are rolling and flashing. A reporter is holding a microphone and speaking straight to camera. People flank her on all sides. Some are chanting. Some are holding placards. A man is crying and beating his breast. A woman takes off her coat and puts it around his shoulders. There is the sound of smashing glass.

The reporter is being jostled as she speaks. She holds out her free hand to keep people back and raises her voice above the noise of the protestors and engines. She is talking about the murder of a young Asian man and his white girlfriend. She expects the prosecution to argue that the murder was racially motivated. The accused, Stephen Parry, is alleged to have associations with far right organisations. As she speaks the back doors to the court burst open. The shouting increases. Parry is being ushered out of court. A cordon of policemen surround him. One of them is covering his head with a grey blanket. The doors of the waiting police van open. Its engine is revving. Parry is pushed down the steps. Men reach out and drag him into the back of the van. Photographers are pressing themselves against the police van. They are lifting their Nikons high above their heads and pointing them through the tinted glass. The flashlights bounce back off the glass.

Timid Old Man and Christian Woman are standing under the trees in the park across the street. For a moment they see Parry's face between the cast iron railings. They see him grin before the blanket is pulled over his head. Christian Woman is holding on to Timid Old Man's walking stick and a plastic carrier bag. She shakes the bag. It makes the sound of metal on metal.

"What's in here anyway?" she says.

"Tools. My tools. I can't be without them. I make toys, you see. Wooden toys. For children."

Timid Old Man is stooping down. He is untying a small bulldog from the railings. He reaches out and plays with its ears. The dog's tail wags. Saliva is dripping from the folds of its face.

"Pinn-y-ochio, Pinn-y-ochio," says Timid Old Man. The dog is panting.

"Look at them," says Christian Woman. She gestures over at the crowd around the van. "Look at them buzzing around him. Like flies on shit."

"Pinn-y-ochio," says Timid Old Man. He reaches into his pocket and pulls out a dog biscuit.

"Don't you care?" says Christian Woman.

"Not about him," says Timid Old Man. He watches the dog munching the biscuit.

"You should. That's what the judge directed. He said his fate was in our hands."

Timid Old Man attaches the leash to the dog's collar.

"The Nazis say he's a martyr, you know. That's what his name means. He was the one that was thrown to the lions," says Christian Woman, "The thing is I don't want to be here. I don't want to judge anybody. I mean, what the hell is justice anyway? I don't want anyone's fate in my hands but my own. How are we meant to tell the truth anyway? I mean, what's so magic about twelve of us? Why not ten or nineteen?"

Timid Old Man looks up at her and laughs. He laughs and pets Pinn-y-ochio.

"I'm sorry," she says, "I'm thinking out loud is all."

The police van is driving away. Officers in the street marshal the crowds.

"Samuntha Samarasinghe for ITN," says the reporter. The cameraman points his camera at the ground. He curses the people pushing and shoving him.

"Children don't play with toys like mine anymore," says Timid Old Man, "Don't have call for it. Guts, blood and guts. The latest thing is you remove the inside of the doll's guts. You can take it apart into little bits. Kidneys and stomach and liver and intestines. They used to do it you know, with animals. The Romans I think. Said you could see the future in the guts. Extispicy? Extipsicy, ecstasy – something like that, eh? The radio says it's all interactive. Interactive. They don't look at things and use their imagination anymore."

He stops petting his dog and looks up at Christian Woman.

"You're a Christian, I see," says Timid Old Man.

"No. I'm not a Christian," says Christian Woman.

"You wear a cross."

"Just because I wear a cross, doesn't mean I'm a Christian."

"What does it mean, then?"

"It was my mother's. She was a Christian. I guess it means I loved my mother."

"Don't you love her anymore?" says Timid Old Man.

Christian Woman looks down at the ground. A raindrop falls from the leaves above them and catches in her hair. Timid Old Man sighs.

"There was someone to judge him in your mother's world," says Timid Old Man.

He looks up at the sky. It is beginning to rain.

On the other side of the street the crowd are dispersing. The photographers and camera crews are getting into their vehicles. Passers-by are opening up their umbrellas. Timid Old Man zips up his raincoat. He takes his cane from Christian Woman and leans it against his hip. The dog stops nuzzling his legs and sits quite still. With his left hand he raises Christian Woman's chin. With his right hand he reaches out and takes her cross. He holds it and looks up into her eyes.

"You have beautiful eyes," he says, "I can say that because it's true and not because I want something from you. That's what being old is," he says.

He lets go of the cross, reaches into his pocket and pulls out a plastic bag. He turns it inside out, bends down, and picks up the dogshit. He puts it in the bin. When he sees that Christian Woman is not watching him he smells his fingertips.

PRAVEEN HERAT

5

A t the beginning of World War II, the Nazis raged across the Russian continent. Their strategy was to employ a *blitzkrieg*, a lightning attack that would force surrender in a matter of months. Hitler believed that the Germans had a monopoly on resilience and patriotism. Hitler was wrong.

In the midst of it all, amid the bombarding forces of the Third Reich, one imagines Mikhail Mikhailovich Bakhtin as a still centre, patience on a monument, quietly collecting, arranging, attending to his writings with the care the lepidopterist lavishes on mounting his specimens. At the time we find him in Kimry, 80 miles north of Moscow, after six years of exile in Kazakhstan (suspected of association with the underground church). It was here, in Kimry, that he finally completed his major work of that period (a study of the eighteenth-century German novel) and lost his left leg to a bone disease that had plagued him for fifteen years. Two manuscript copies of the work existed. One disappeared when the Germans razed his publishing house to the ground. The other Bakhtin used as rolling paper for cigarettes. He was an inveterate smoker. He died from emphysema in 1975 with a cigarette burning between his lips.

Despite this lost manuscript, a great number of his works survive: no small proof that this man, a man who endured both World Wars, the Russian Revolution, civil war, famine, illness, exile and intellectual suppression, who doggedly pursued his own unique and eccentric path through literary history against the prevailing academic currents of his time – no small proof that this man is one of the great minds of the twentieth century.

What these writings demonstrate is a *restless* mind, esoteric, leftfield – a mind that denies convenient summation: like most great thinkers he was prepared to question himself, and inclined to refine or even contradict his previous assumptions in the quest to further understanding.

He was obsessed, amongst other things, with the history of the novel. But he wasn't interested in tracing the novel's origins back in time. For him 'The Novel' is not a list of books that

144

universities give to their students. It is not a child of time. The novel is an idea, a spirit, a tendency, an exaggeration of what is already inherent in the language each one of us speaks.

Language for Bakhtin is always a social phenomenon, always about people talking to other people; it cannot be placed under glass and examined like a museum exhibit because it is a living thing, only grasped in dialogue; not just 'dialogue' in the sense of one person talking to another: even someone writing a diary is holding a conversation with himself about the language he uses, reading himself as he writes. Every time we open our mouths, pick up a pen, start typing an email, every time we begin to wield any word, that word cannot help but be invested with all the ways it has been used before by other people. Any one word in any one context is therefore infused with innumerable meanings: language is 'multi-accentual'. Against this is the illusion of 'unitary' language, the narrow, supposedly closed-off language of the ruling class, the dictionary, the news reporter, this essay... Of course we need this illusion – we need some idea of a 'unitary' language to maximise mutual understanding, to communicate, but behind this is that volatile force, that uncontrollable proliferation of meaning: what Bakhtin called 'heteroglossia' (literally meaning 'many languages').

It is this heteroglosssia which the novel puts into overdrive. Other forms of literature cannot do this. Take the sonnet for instance: this is a fixed form, closed-off, limited to its fourteen lines. The language of a sonnet has to fit itself to this form. Indeed part of our appreciation of any writer of sonnets is seeing how s/he negotiates this limitation. We find the same kind of limiting form in every other genre to some extent, except, for Bakhtin, in the novel, where exactly the opposite is the case: the novel grows out of the language(s) in which it is written; it takes *their* shape.

What makes the novel so special?

Firstly, it has no formal dictates: it is not fourteen lines or any other amount of lines so it is plastic, always – as the word 'novel' suggests – taking on *new* forms. This is because it hasn't been ossified into a skeletal form, it hasn't been handed down to us ready-made, which is the same as saying that *it doesn't exist before history begins.* Therefore, it is always in the process of developing.

Secondly, the novel is the youngest of all literary genres, virtually the only genre that comes into its own *after the advent of the book itself.* So, while all other genres possess residual characteristics of being orally presented, the novel is hyperconscious of the fact that it is written, and *only* written, so it becomes conditioned by the fact that its meaning is manipulated by a reader who has no physical connection to the author. Yes, this is true of anything written, but the novel developed *because* of this, not *before.* So, the novel is always having a conversation with this unknowable person (that's *you,* the reader, the place where all the voices meet and harmoniously combine). This is part of the novel's indeterminacy, its open-endedness, the freedom it thrives on. Because it enjoys such freedom, the novel runs riot: it misbehaves itself, it revels in its status as the irreverent, bastard, cross-caste child of literature – it breaks all the rules, uses all the languages that 'literature' is not supposed to, delights in the profane (as young children are often prone to do), parodies all the other literary types, satirises all that is held to be sacred, engages with the taboo... It is a roomful of voices, like a jury or a focus group, a cabinet meeting, a prayer meeting, group therapy, chamber music. It is drunken people barracking and haranguing each other in a pub and market hawkers and workmen shouting out in the street.

Bakhtin shows us that the novel is the black sheep in the literary family. He goes on to identify its rebel gene not in one work or at one point in time but as an element in a whole range of different writings, especially where social hierarchies are inverted – carnivalised – and the sacred is profaned, where absolutely nothing is exempt from comic ridicule, where the human body in sex, death and defecation is unashamedly examined. He finds the gene across eras and national divides. He finds it in the satire of Rabelais, in the 'Menippean' satire of writers such as Lucian (115-after180) and, ultimately, in the Socratic dialogues.

Socrates (469-399 B.C.), an Athenian stonemason and distinguished soldier, had been honoured by his country in the Peloponnesian War for outstanding bravery. Not only was he a man of courage but one of deep conviction, prepared to defend his own beliefs (particularly in matters of justice) regardless of the will of those in authority. Such obstinacy won him both young disciples and a host of enemies in positions of power, and it is at the mercy of such enemies that we find him in 399BC, sentenced to death for undermining belief in the Greek gods and corrupting the Athenian youth. Even when the authorities offered him exile, Socrates remained inveterately defiant, proclaiming that he should not only be freed but dined for life at the expense of the state on account of his good works. Such insolence secured his fate.

His last month of incarceration – during which time he conversed incessantly with friends and followers – is his enduring legacy to mankind. In fact he left not a single piece of writing behind him: what we have of him are only the dialogues of Plato and Xenophon. In these works we observe the Socratic method of inquiry: the quest to attain true knowledge by defining abstract concepts via an exchange of views. The dialogues always begin with a question (such as: What is courage? What is justice? What is rhetoric? Can virtue be taught?); when the interlocutor has provided his definition the interrogation continues and, via a process of question and answer, the original definition is shown to be inadequate. But there is no happy conclusion here: Socrates does not wave a magic wand and pull the correct definition out of a top hat. He conceals no 'teacher's edition' in the folds of his robe. Instead, the process results in *aporia* (literally meaning 'pathless path'): a state of indeterminacy, from which everyone concerned has established the extent of his or her ignorance, a form of indeterminacy which on another level is akin to the 'open-endedness' we have already ascribed to the novel itself. This indeterminacy – an indeterminacy which might be called 'postmodern' – is the novel's most ancient gene, a source of both pleasure and annihilation. In fact, one could say the novel is *always* postmodern – even thousands of years before the term was coined.

Bakhtin saw all this and wrote it down. As with most great thinkers – like Newton and the famous apple – he was only describing what anyone could have seen. But he was not alone. As he toiled on feverishly, an intellectual Stakhanovite, another genius in (self-imposed) exile was flitting around the European continent, drawing the same conclusions about the novel form *in the form of a novel itself*: James Joyce. It is in the process of writing his masterpiece, *Ulysses* (published in Paris, 1922, the story of writing rather than the writing of a story), that Joyce seems to divine the same ideas we have seen in Bakhtin.

Ulysses starts innocuously enough in terms of style. Indeed, the first nine episodes are stylistically no more innovative than the writing (the *style indirect libre*) of Joyce's French predecessor Gustave Flaubert (1821-80). However, by the time he came to write the tenth episode, Joyce's attitude to his novel had altered and the style begins to metamorphose in radical ways. This tenth episode – known by the name of 'Wandering Rocks' – is composed of nineteen different stories, each following a different character as s/he walks through the Dublin streets. Events and scenes repeat themselves from one story to another, so we see the same scene through the eyes and minds of different people. This means that the Dublin streetscene can only be composed of a whole range of perspectives, by a 'plurality of consciousness', each one subjective and limited when merely taken on its own. The world exists, and is communicated, only via all these differing perspectives and the *languages* of these perspectives, akin to what Bakhtin suggested about the novel being made up of voices interrogating subject matter: everything we see and experience is like a Socratic concept that can be endlessly interrogated but never incontrovertibly defined. This has its counterpart in the visual art of the time, in the cubism of Picasso say, where objects are presented from numerous angles of vision on the same plane – as if the view is made of panes of shifting glass.

We think that Bakhtin never read Joyce and Joyce never read Bakhtin. Yet somehow they came to the same conclusions about the ways in which we grasp the world around us. How? Was it just that the culture they lived in forced them to make connections, come to realisations, that man had never had to face before? Was it the experience of a world torn by war that coloured their intellectual perspective?

And what of the fact that the Joyce-Bakhtin parallel is not alone in history, that it has an analogue that pre-dates it by 2300 years? For it was then that Bakhtin's great precursor Socrates took his fatal draught of hemlock, leaving behind him a flood of dialogues. And it was then also that the so-called redactor of Genesis made the final compilation of the Bible's own myth of clashing languages: the story of Babel.

How can we begin to explain this mysterious synchronicity? How do we make these Babels connect?

JOYCE LAMBERT

Seven Poems

Joyce Lambert is married and has a grown-up family. She was born in Stockport and spent her childhood there. Now after travelling widely she is settled in Rutland with husband, garden and laptop.

Learning to breathe

Megan sleeps
in a glass box
wired to life.

A bead of milk sways
in a plastic tube,
a spirit level.

Walking the coast-to-coast, Phil had
slowed us right down, one behind the other,

one foot behind the other. Slow. Slow.
Watch the next bend. No stopping

till the gorse bush by that hunched
white rock. Then a rest. Chocolate.

Up the scree slope, finding a footing,
boots scrabbling behind, crunching in front,

matching demand to supply,
breathing takes care of itself.

Now, Megan stretches, her ribs push up.
She kicks her legs; yawns.
Gives a purple smile.

Low tide

Waiting for the turn.
I never look up –
the power of the sea.
Flotsam a magnet –
crazy glass, grey planks
up to my doorstep.
Treasures. Wind-tossed
trawl-nets, corks, timbers.
Dawn shimmering swell.

They don't think I'm safe –
tidying up stuff –
my cans. Folks will talk.
Mary sweeps them away.
All those rich pickings,
browns, reds and yellows,
rusted and sand-struck.
My stock-pile. Resources.
Bringing me curtains!

Young men with cameras.
How long to make it
from the first inkling?
They're mad on ideas.
There was no idea.
Just the sea took him.
How could I watch it?
He sent me offerings,
I grabbed them. Hammered

them over the window,
shutting it all out.
Mary – "some company ... "
How much does she know?

Dark in the hut. Calm,
peace and quiet. Talking?
What good does that do?
Then a funny thing –
chink in the boards,

a splinter of light.
Sun coming up,
coral pink, lovely.
Sat there and watched it.
Pink grey cream navy,
so many colours.
Next day another.
Two bits of heaven.
And so on. Nibbled

by winter storms,
letting the light in.
I started with green
sea-shattered bottles,
finding the pieces,
matching the right holes,
building by tide-turns,
made my own rainbow.
It took me over.

Mary goes frantic –
'Knocking out shingles!'
I had to be cunning,
build up the inside
strip off the outside,
taking my chances,
each day's surprises.
And keeping some spy-holes
for watching the sky change.

Primary care

An elephant calf stays at least a day
in a stronghold of legs which mark time,

charm a circle, shape his space,
shuffle, nudge him in the right direction

somehow, a wall to lean on
and a scoop to lift him when he falls.

He wobbles in this baby walker
of wrinkled hide, follows a swinging tail.

She doesn't hurry, ambles among trees,
browses, waits, sets an easy pace, until

he pads more steadily, his trunk
investigates a widening path,

he speeds up, knows he can overtake her
any time he likes. The herd fans out,

and in. Old-fashioned, apron string mothers
surround him, extend a leafy distance.

Flowers for Mum

In Auntie's living room, Saturday clocks ticked out
the comfortable rhythms of knitting,
white, on fine needles tucked under arms,
across ladylike blouses in apricot, eau-de-nil,
pieces pressed under the carpet between sheets of newspaper,
one by one until they were finished, could be stitched together.

Behind the kitchen door, his Saturday flowers –
dahlias "to take home for your mum"–
rust velvet, wrapped in last week's *Chronicle*,
held at arm's length, dropping earwigs on the lino,
until he had his kiss for them, mouth hard on your lips,
the press of his hand through your neat school uniform.

Winter break

I worry about flying. There's nothing
between you and the ground, but then,
much too much, if it comes to it.

Not like the wife. Duck to water,
waiting for take-off. Packing no problem but
sorting out the bird-sitters – murder!

Up to Safeway – nuts, seeds – you name it –
bacon all week to collect the rinds.
Rota for filling the bird-bath. Barmy.

I used to choose, do the organising,
she tagged along. Didn't seem
to mind. Now she rules the roost.

Islands. Water up to the doorsteps,
seabirds, pelicans in and out.
I don't know what to make of it.

She almost cancelled this week, but I told her
you don't need to feed a heron,
he'll be down for next door's goldfish.

An owl hit the window, left a silhouette,
she wouldn't wash it off. Funny –
she used to be pretty house-proud.

Little yellow bird last spring, tapping
on every window trying to get in. Really upset her.
Crying at geese flying over. Clouds, trees.

When the kids went the first thing she said –
now we can fly – spread our wings.
I blame her father – he kept pigeons.

I go more for ponds, frogspawn, tiddlers,
wondering how many will survive.
Great crested newt - there's a creature!

Landing at Gatwick I swear she can
spot the house at five miles; the magpie
circling the blackbird's nest:

could strangle it with her bare hands.

Redecorate

Layers of sea colours waver through green
around the spectrum; blur beyond blue.
Three flying pelicans make life a beach –

sand carpet, designer buckets and spades.
Bring in striped deckchairs, rose shells on a quilt,
moonstone and peridot, a driftwood frame.

What to do about the paled photograph –
four backs turned, bare feet scrambling across rocks?
Hopeless to find the negative, try to wind back.

Settle for ragging and sponging, old gold.
Stamped patterns, fish among rocks in wave-spray,
the fisherman with his red plastic bowl.

Aquarium

An iron seagull hangs over thick chocolate sea
too dense to see through, trawls the Golden Mile,
while under the airy tonnage of the Tower a cube
of Fylde Coast Rocky Reef is boxed for scrutiny:
butterfish, hermit crabs, five-bearded rockling
captured from their holes in low spring tides.
Tiger-striped shrimps, minute wire sculptures,
sidle across rocks, torment anemones, prod
and pull back to the edge of their precipice.
Creatures of silver wire and polythene knit water,
an unnamed tiddler climbs the tank, chalk
on a blackboard, and the lesser weever-fish
dashes from under a sprinkle of sand.

In other tanks, exotics. Banded leporinos –
small mouths, few teeth, they're meant
to swim heads down to forage. Red-tailed catfish
sweep patches in the gravel with scallop-shell
tails, ivory and pink. Whiskers trail the same
stones, five, six times a minute. The thorn-back ray
slides along chipped paintwork, morays after thirty
years gape, and, rarely, shimmy like ribbons off a gift.
Lion fish, 'Villains of the Seas', withhold their venom,
spread soft geometry of fins in stripes and spots,
slow water butterflies. Pacu, yellow tangs. Four
giant turtles paddle an endless spiral among angels,
clowns and damsel fish, bubbles escaping.

Highbury Fields Forever

Sonia Lambert lives in London. She has written stories for BBC Radio 4 – *One Day Travelcard* was a 'Book at Bedtime' in 1995, as part of the First Bite Festival, *Election Night* was broadcast in 1997 and *Visiting Royalty* was broadcast in 1998. The following piece is a short story. She is currently working on a novel.

The first time I saw the flat in Clapham it was completely empty. That's what did it for me. There was something breathtaking about sunlight falling on a bare floor, a slanting shadow on a skirting board, the dust particles dancing in the light. Many things seemed excruciatingly beautiful, around then.

I was in a state of shock, which isn't the ideal time to buy property. An estate agent shows you a handful of potential futures, and you choose one. Until I saw the empty flat, things had frozen, and I had trouble imagining any sort of future at all – then suddenly I thought, this is it.

Out of the bedroom window, I could see a patchwork of gardens, and a tall, square building surrounded by sycamore trees.

"What's that?" I asked the estate agent.

He was young, not more than twenty, and he swung between a puppyish enthusiasm when speaking and a desperate boredom when silent, fiddling with the keys. It seemed a kindness to ask him a question. "It's a hospice," he said, and considered it for a moment, looking for a selling point. "So they don't make a lot of noise."

For the first time, I managed not to tell him anything. I had this compulsion to tell people, so that after a moment of terrified embarrassment, in which their pain was for once greater than mine, they'd let me off the normal rules. You know there's a point in the conversation when this will happen, and usually, the sooner it's over with, the better. This time, though, I didn't tell. "What the hell," I thought. "He doesn't have to know."

I was proud of myself for that. The new flat wasn't as empty as it looked, though. I'm beginning to learn that you don't get away that easily.

I moved five months after Matthew died. I can say that now – it's become a historical fact, but it took a while to solidify. At the time, I couldn't say it without the guilty feeling that I was somehow making it a tiny bit truer. Anniversaries – days, weeks, months – were planted everywhere, like land mines.

I had to leave our old flat. It was a way to take stock of what was left – ripping the tangled mess apart in bleeding handfuls.

People get very attached to areas in London. It's a way to get your bearings, and every part of town can be like a different city. I decided to do something drastic, and move across the river. Matthew was a committed North Londoner – "But what if a bridge was closed, or something, and you got completely cut off?" I remember him asking a baffled couple from Battersea. My sister lives in Clapham, and I ended up there.

Friends tried to talk me out of it, saying it was too soon, that I wasn't ready.

"Grief can be like a nervous breakdown," said Babs, turning from the cooker with the coffee pot, and pouring me another cup (everyone became very capable around me). Babs had never quite grown out of the Goth phase we went through at school – thick eyeliner, dangly earrings, her ample bosom clad in black. She was a recent divorcee, and took a kind of pleasure in spotting the stages, mapping the mood swings. She put the milk back on the side, clearing a space, and I saw that the plate would fall, and it fell, and fractured on the floor. I cringed as if I'd been hit. "Oh shit," said Babs, and began to tidy up.

"The thing is, you won't realise how out of it you are until you look back, in a few more months," she said. "You have to go really slowly. You know what they say about moving? It's the third most stressful thing…" Babs was taking a course in counselling. She suggested, again, that I see a 'fully-qualified' counsellor.

I shook my head. It wasn't her fault. People couldn't handle me, they preferred to treat violent emotion as an illness. I could see why I made them nervous. I might as well have had 'You Are Mortal' stamped on my forehead.

I heard so many stories. It seemed that people, lost for words, had to offer me their own experiences of death. Brain tumours, car crashes, even peanut allergies – I was building up quite a collection. I heard about women who slept with their husband's shirt for a year; plucky little widows who crossed the Sahara on a bike, and raised thousands for leukaemia research. Pilgrimages of one sort or another – trips to Rajasthan or spiritual experiences in the Highlands – were much to the taste of our graduate, mostly atheist friends. Everything I heard was like an echo of my own pain. The world was full of previously unnoticed horrors.

In books and films, when someone's going to die, they're often a bit other-worldly to start with. I sometimes heard people trying to re-write Matt's past in the 'too good for this world' mode, and I tried to resist. I sympathised, perhaps because I'm not the grieving type either.

I wish that you'd known him. I try to itemise him, but it never does the job. His curly hair, his crappy jokes, his sweet knock-knees and ragged boxer shorts – most of all, the smell of him. I was carrying it all, and I wanted to give it to people. I had more in common with someone dead than with anyone alive. People at work would avoid me, with a look of real panic.

It took me a while to realise that it came not from Matthew, but from me. I made them all afraid.

Sleep was a difficult area. My sister, on one of the early nights – driven to distraction by my frantic, stricken energy and my crazy, suspicious eyes – tried to coax me into bed. I tried to evade her, because bed was a trap full of horrors. She flinched, as she closed the wardrobe door on shirts and suits. Guiltily, she fed me a temazepam with a mug of soup.

For a while, I carried on taking the pills. I was afraid of the night. After dark, my grief would thunder through the flat like a rhinoceros – brutal, futile force – crashing blindly against the walls, again and again. The night I moved, I stopped taking them. I thought, there's plenty to do, what does it matter if I stay awake?

The new flat was full of cardboard boxes. Babs had been by with a bottle, and spent a long time telling me how easy the tube trip was. After she left, I moved restlessly around the bright living room, mentally reorganising my possessions. The room felt exposed without curtains, on show like a stage or a screen. Outside, I could see the dark leaves on the sycamores, blowing in the windy night, and I could hear distant traffic, like the sea. I switched off the light.

I went into the bedroom and lay down. I fell asleep easily. Maybe it was because it was the first night that I hadn't taken a pill, but the first special dream came then, sometime in the early hours. I could tell it was different from my ordinary dreams. It seemed unusually vivid.

I dreamed about our old flat in Highbury, which seemed more real to me than the flat in which I slept. First of all, I was walking along the hall. I noticed cardboard boxes – unsurprising, given the number I'd seen the day before. There was a strange rush matting on the floor, that was wrong, and a bit disturbing.

Then I was in the kitchen. I was smashing it up, pulling plates from the cupboard and flinging them onto the floor, smashing the glass in the cabinets, shattering mugs against the wall.

When I woke up, the room was flooded with sunlight – I had tacked a sheet over the window, which had become a brilliant white square. Instantly, things seemed different. Every time I woke, the realisation of Matt's death hit me again, and that morning was no exception, but mixed in with that was something else. I lay there, bewildered and emptied. The atmosphere of the dream still hung around me, like cigarette smoke, in the air.

That day, I started unpacking.

I never realised, until Matt died, how much a person *is* his belongings. Matthew's things, all over the flat, seemed to be waiting for him. I had to make them realise, to get them under control.

"Already?" said his mother, on the telephone.

"They're only things," I said, unconvinced.

"Only things?" she said querulously. "The Crown Jewels are only things, and the Mona Lisa…"

"You can take them," I said.

There was a pause for a moment, as she struggled to regain

some kind of propriety. "It's all right, dear," she said, at length. "I understand that you can't live in a shrine." That, though, was exactly what she wanted me to do.

"Anything, anything at all that you want, you must tell me."

Again, she was silent for a moment. "Could I have a sweater?" she said eventually, in a small voice.

I found her a nice sweater, and a week later, I gave it to her. I knew that she wanted to bury her face in it, but she resisted, stroking and smoothing the material distractedly with her fingers. "Did you wash it?" she said guiltily, in a contorted voice. With a shock, I recognised the yearning in that question.

"I'm sorry," I said. "It was clean already."

Toby was Matthew's best friend. After the funeral, he only came round once, and it was difficult for us both. He was scared – of me, or perhaps of breaking down in front of me. He made me feel like an ex-wife, bewildered by the sudden negation of the past.

People had stopped saying "How are you?" Instead, they said "How are you coping?" which was even less answerable. They thought that they couldn't talk about themselves, either, so conversation got pretty difficult.

For some reason, I started telling Toby about the clerk, about registering the death. "...He made me repeat it, it really makes you take it in."

"What a grim job," he said.

"Apparently they get to do the births as well."

Toby looked out of the window, over Highbury Fields. "I don't know what to do with all his stuff... There are some quite good jackets," I said.

"Please," he said, and it was a whimper, a plea for mercy, "I can't take any of his clothes."

"Oh, OK," I said, but I felt like shouting at him, *you fucking wimp! I have to live here!*

He shifted in his seat. "I'd better be off. Olivia will be wondering..." he swallowed his words. Again I wanted to shout at him, to shake him, sitting there so ruddy-cheeked and clean shaven in his crisp denim shirt. I just looked at him, which was probably worse. Perhaps he was right to be scared of me, after all.

After that, Babs came round one Sunday, and we set about the business, like forensic scientists, with black plastic bin-liners. All this is so complicated, and yet it's that simple. Get rid of his things, in an afternoon, and there's nothing left.

So, moving into my new flat in Clapham, it was with the greatest care that I cleaned and unpacked and put out my stuff, room by room. It was a strange, censored version of myself: my things, without Matthew's. Even so, familiar pictures, familiar books, were like my old life, following a few steps behind.

That night, I dreamed a special dream again. Once again, I dreamed of our flat on Highbury Fields.

We had a box room, overflowing with Matt's papers, where we dumped things we couldn't bear to get rid of. I had left Matthew's corpse in this room. His yellowing skin was squashed out of shape, like a pair of tights put on twisted. The nurse came to inject him with preservatives, but she made a mistake, and he woke up, or came back to life.

I was sitting in the living room, and there were other people there as well. Matthew padded along the hall, and blundered in, all sweetly little-boy tearful. "Why did you leave me alone in there?" he said accusingly. "You promised to wake me up."

"My poor love," I said, and I tried to make him comfortable and cosy, in front of the fire. "There you are," I said, "isn't that nice? You can lie in state, here, with us." Then suddenly I felt terrible, because the phrase 'lie in state' sounded as if I meant that he was dead, and I was afraid that he might get offended and leave again.

After that, I was just standing in the long hallway (that strange and wrong rush matting again) in the darkness, filled with a wrenching sense of desolation. I was listening to someone else breathing softly in the bedroom, and feeling alone, adrift on an ice-floe.

I woke up and found that I was sobbing aloud. Oh God, I thought, this will go on forever.

I sat on the top deck of one of the buses that sway and lurch around South London. I looked down at the drenched city from the window – a puddle on the roof of a bus shelter; a couple kissing at the stop, leaning into one another; red brick houses, and gardens with dripping rosebushes. Drops of water slid down the grimy glass.

Something strange happened to time when Matthew died. At first, I thought it had stopped, and things would never change. Gradually, I began to notice movement: political crises came and went, new albums were released – they began to change the packaging of various products. I realised the scale of this betrayal. Step by step, they were building a world he wouldn't recognise.

I began to see his life as a whole, complete. There was a kind of telescoping effect: things that had happened when we first met seemed as recent as things that had happened last year.

I looked at the obituaries page in newspapers, but only to calculate the life-span of each person mentioned, and feel resentful. I spent time in graveyards – crowded and impersonal, like the rest of London – and if, very occasionally, I found the headstone of someone whose allocated years were fewer than Matthew's, I felt a strange kind of relief. I couldn't stand the sight of children, and middle-aged men made me incoherent with rage. I tried to fight it, but I could feel it twisting me.

The bus came to a jolting halt. I looked at the other people on the top deck, and thought: you will all die. I looked at their living, moving faces.

The bus moved forward, and stopped again, outside the hospice, juddering as it waited in traffic. I could see shapes moving at the windows. I could see into the garden, green and wet.

From my seat on the top deck, I saw a woman with an umbrella at the hospice gate. I wanted to reach out to her, to tell her 'it's OK, I know'. I couldn't, of course. There was no way I could tell people whatever it was that I knew.

Tears were sliding down my cheeks, faster than the drops on the glass, and I was missing my stop. I could only blot my crumpled, disfigured face with my hands, turn my face from the staring people, and try to control my juddering shoulders.

I slept a lot, by then. I spent nearly as much time asleep as I did awake, living my parallel life.

Matthew and I were walking slowly down the long hallway. It was lined with everyone we knew – family, friends and colleagues – all those people through whom, as a couple, you sew your lives together. They were laughing and waving, there were banners and streamers. As Matthew and I passed through the archway of cheering people, we smiled modestly, holding hands. Sometimes we stopped to greet someone, on the way.

Then we reached the living room. The furniture was different, cream coloured, not my kind of thing, and someone had put up strange posters in clip-frames – Georgia O'Keeffe, I think – showing enormous flowers. Matthew turned to me. "Shall we dance?" he said.

He wore jeans, and a faded brown shirt, one of my favourites. We danced very slowly, and I rested my head on his shoulder, breathing in his sweaty, soapy smell. It was bliss just to be near him. He spoke to me, and I was so pleased, so grateful, to hear the musical, humorous modulations of his voice just one more time. But then, that thought reminded me that he was going to die.

"Shouldn't you be dead by now?" I said. Instantly, I was flooded with remorse and fear. How could I say such a thing? How could I go and spoil it when it was all so lovely?

He just smiled an ironic, slightly wronged smile. "What a thing to say, Iz!" he said, and enfolded me in his arms. I rested my head once again on his shoulder, and was engulfed in the memory of him.

He was even in the supermarket, *especially* in the supermarket, making remarks about the South Londoners, and getting excited about the organic meat. As I wandered the shining aisles in a daze, picking things up and putting them down, he was at my shoulder. "What do you fancy for tonight, sweetheart?" I wasn't all that hungry. Actually, I couldn't even remember what it was I liked to eat.

Matthew was in my head, teasing and berating me, still forcing me, from beyond the grave, to buy eco-friendly washing powder. He was near the sauces and pickles, hovering over the freezers, pointing mutely at the Tabasco bottle, too weak to speak – the hospice food was much too bland for him, even at the end. He was there with me, the day after his diagnosis, the world warped with horror, as we filled the trolley with his favourite things. We blundered through the supermarket, living in the only way we knew, in a sort of dreadful parody of our lives, as a scream of sheer terror built up inside.

My number flashed up in huge red digits, above the gently humming delicatessen counter. "What can I get you?" said a woman in a paper hat. I shook my head quickly and walked away, unable to speak.

Stop the trolley. Breathe deeply. Loss of control is everywhere – the muttering schizophrenic at the entrance, the lurching wino by the recycling bins. Londoners will disown you in an instant, for the strangeness in your eyes.

Matt and I were sitting around in our old living room, with a large group of friends. We were sitting on the vile, cream-coloured sofa, and I was the only one even slightly bothered by the new pictures.

Matthew was fine, but we were looking at Polaroids from his illness. In the photos his face was a funny colour, for example pale blue, or his eyes were much too big.

We were all laughing and talking. "You looked terrible," I said to Matthew, teasingly.

"OK, OK, I know," he said, irritably.

After a while, I wanted all the other people to leave, so that we could be alone together. "I'm sorry, we've got to get on," I said to them all. "It's just that we're beginning to have had enough of illness and death."

That made Matthew really angry. "You mean *you* have!" he said, furiously, and ran outside to fling himself on to the barbed wire that surrounded the building.

I told Babs about some of my dreams, one evening when she came round for supper. They were precious, and I was worried about diluting their power, but they also scared me. There was something about them that wasn't right.

Babs, of course, lapped it up. She'd developed a habit of echoing my sentences back at me, with an added question mark. I told her about the barbed wire.

"And how did that make you feel?" she said. The way she said it made me realise, with a surge of rage, that it was a question that they taught her to ask on her counselling course.

"Fuck off!" I screamed, standing up and overturning my chair like a child. In a second, I became a furious mad thing. "Fuck off, fuck off, fuck off!" I shouted.

"I feel as if you're trying to drive me away," she said.

"How perceptive," I said, manoeuvring her out of the door.

"Isobel..." she said, her face collapsing into tears. I handed her her coat, and closed the door on her. I wanted to be alone. All I wanted was to sleep and, if I could, to dream.

Of course I couldn't sleep – even that I blamed on Babs – and later that night I rang her in tears.

"Oh Izzy," she said, "I'm sorry. I just feel so helpless, watching you like this."

"I'm sorry too," I said, remembering how I'd been, over the last few months. "I'm not myself." As I spoke the words, I realised they were true. Myself was the person with Matthew, and I couldn't be her anymore – and I hadn't grown into myself, the new person I'd be without him. I was between personalities, looking for a life.

"I don't know how you've coped," said Babs. I didn't know, either. Everything had become so weird. It was like waking up, one morning, in the wrong world.

I went back to the hospice, our hospice in North London; I went with Matthew's mother. Six months after a death, they invite you back. So there we all were, like some kind of weird school reunion – the graduates of May.

We sat on orange plastic chairs in another part of the building. There were other relatives there – they looked familiar, though I'd hardly spoken to them at the time – a few private dramas taking place on the margins of our great odyssey, other people marked, like us, as able to cry in the strangest situations. There was a box of Kleenex on every table.

Still, it was strange to see them. At the time, I'd glimpsed what was going on and for some reason, I'd thought their tragedies were greater than ours – a sick mother with her kids had moved me to tears. Now, six months on and more deeply embedded in my grief, I was determined that things couldn't be as bad for them. The person who died must have been older, less loved, or at least they had kids.

We made bizarre small-talk: "Who did you lose?" or "What a coincidence, ours was Hodgkin's too!" I sat next to a blonde widow: everything she said was like an accusation. She couldn't afford childcare, and was living on benefits. She'd missed her husband's death, because she'd gone to take a shower.

I didn't know what to say. The sensation reminded me of something, and then I thought: oh, so this is how Babs must feel. "And how did that make you feel?" I said.

She looked at me with disgust. "Angry."

We wandered through the wards, among the sick and the dying. It was hard to believe that there were a new lot in there, that this was a constant process – I'd have thought they'd all be dead by now. I was drawn to the sick in a peculiar way. I was searching for a look in their shining eyes, a familiar jawbone, a pinched smile, and a strong, acrid smell.

The garden, though, was the heart of it all, a place for beginnings and endings. I stood with Matthew's mother by the sundial, surrounded by the rustle of the black leaves, the grass shining under the moon. We saw lit rooms, behind drawn curtains.

As usual, there was a moment when I remembered something. "Oh God," I said, "but won't we upset them? Those other patients who are still alive, won't they be disturbed by the relatives of the dead wandering around wringing their hands?"

Matthew's mother looked at me, and when she spoke, I realised it was a dream. "Don't worry dear, they can't see us," she said. "Haven't you noticed yet?"

Babs and I were walking on Clapham Common. It was cold, and clear, and very bright – a winter's day like a chip of sparkling ice. The earth was frozen, and the grass crunched underfoot. In the distance, cars crawled like insects around the fringes, and tiny houses and hotels pierced the horizon. From where we stood, the luminous green grass, in the late afternoon sun, was like the whole, curving world.

"It's like a kind of constant double vision," I said, trying to catch my thoughts. "I see the past and the present at the same time, on top of each other – I wonder if that's something that old people get? It's like being possessed, haunted, but I feel as if I'm the ghost. I'm stumbling around, watching from the outside. I'm aware of this reality in life that everyone else seems to forget…I don't fit into the world at all."

Babs's coat was flapping in the wind, and she waddled beside me, like a large crow. Everything was tinged with weird, vivid, before-dusk colours; the spectrum having a last wild fling before being muted with grey.

"We talked about this, on my course, the other day," said Babs. "About how ghosts are a product of sorrow." She glanced at me, to check she wasn't freaking me out. She's more careful with me now, watching what she says. "About how it's the bereaved, not the dead, who tend to do the haunting."

The icy wind lifted my hair from my temples. The Common was so beautiful, it hurt my heart to look at it; there were moments when I felt, superstitiously, that I was looking at it for Matt. Over our heads, the clouds were moving, paler, already touched with sodium orange, in the purple, darkening sky. My thoughts were churning in my head, until one emotion surfaced, clearer than the others. How could I have guessed that in a world without Matthew, there would still be evenings like this?

I found myself driving past the old flat on Highbury Fields. It was always unlikely that I could stay away. I stopped the car. There was even a parking space.

It was a Saturday afternoon. It hadn't been properly light all day – I could look straight at the disc of the pale, wintry sun. Indoors, people had their lights on. I looked over at

Highbury Fields, and saw trees, scribbled like thread-veins against the sky. There was a match on, and the streets were deserted – occasionally, you could hear the muffled roar of the crowd. I felt guilty: I knew I was breaking the rules, but why not, I thought, since I come here every night? I was reassured to hear my footsteps crunch on the gravel.

The stairwell smelled the same, and I had to resist the urge to check the post. A young woman came to the door. She took a step backwards when she saw me, and my heart went out to her. Her eyes moved quickly, and all she said was "Oh," but I recognised someone, for once, in as bad a state as I was. It gave me strength just to see her.

I told her my name. "You bought the flat from me. I was just passing, and I wondered if I might have a look, to see how the old place has changed...to see how you were getting along," I said, trying to force my impulse into some kind of acceptable shape.

The woman was distracted. I wondered if this was a mistake, she didn't seem entirely normal. She inhaled, sharply. "I'm so glad you came," she said. "The estate agent said that it would be unwise to try and trace you, but I wanted to talk to you...Please, come in."

I stepped in, and saw the rush matting that they'd put down in the hall. I had a terrible feeling, a pounding certainty in my chest, that I already knew what the living room would look like.

The woman led me into the kitchen instead, where they had put in new units.

"Would you like a cup of tea?" she said. She took down some mugs, and I saw that her hands were shaking. "Please, sit down. It's a beautiful flat. I can tell that a lot went into it."

"Yes... thank you," I said.

She placed tea-bags in the mugs, and turned to me. "Now," she said, with apparent effort, "what I wanted to ask you was, did you ever have any...problems here?" She looked at me pleadingly.

"Problems?" I said. "What kind of problems?"

She seemed to be about to answer, and then changed her mind. "Never mind," she said, briskly.

"No, it's OK. You can tell me."

She gave a weak half-smile. "You name it. Breakages, noises – footsteps, sobbing, slamming…" her voice, and her gaze, faltered. "I'm not usually a nervous person." She tried to laugh, without conviction.

I gripped my seat, because the room was slipping away. "Oh my God," I managed to say. "He's still here. I knew it."

The woman looked straight at me. There was a kind of pity in her face, and I felt the balance of power between us shift slightly, again.

"It isn't a he, it's a she," the woman said.

The kettle boiled, and clicked off. The woman spoke again, surprisingly gently. "Would you like sugar?" she said, turning to pour the water.

I no longer dream so much, these days, which is good because it was exhausting. Still, the dreams come occasionally, like a luminous gift, and I rely on them. A glimpse of his back at the far end of the hallway, his smell on a towel in the bathroom, his laughter, in another room – I still need that. On the one hand, I realise it's a kind of insanity – on the other, please God, don't let it ever end.

There was something strange about the time when Matthew died. I saw and felt it all with such violent clarity. We sat together in the hospice garden, the day before, with our senses raw, and everything clamouring around us: every blade of grass, every leaf, every twist of the wind. The world was sharpened – by love, by loss, by fear, I don't know – to the point of pain. It's a good memory, in spite of all the misery that went with it. It makes me think that perhaps, this is all the heaven we will get.

Last night I dreamed that I was flying, with Matthew, over London. I had a wonderful contraption, like a parachute that could go up as well as down. I don't know if Matthew was somehow strapped in with me, but I could hear his voice in my ear, and feel his breath against my cheek.

There were wisps of cloud, obscuring our view, and roads like plump grey veins, far below, and a glinting reservoir. There were railway lines, like stringy tendons. I saw patches of grass, with trees collecting like dust balls in the folds. Matthew was pointing things out.

"Look," he said, excitedly, "that's Highbury Fields, where we used to live."

I had to concentrate to navigate, but he was directing me. "Down a bit, left a bit… Look, that must be the Holloway Road." We saw the roof of our building, and Matthew got enthusiastic, and wanted to land.

"We're not supposed to," I said.

So we carried on, pointing out places where we used to go, things that had changed, things that were new. I wanted it to last forever.

"How could I have missed all this?" said Matthew, as our feet brushed the television aerials, and the tops of the trees.

KATE MCCORMACK
from *36D*

Kate McCormack was brought up in Cheltenham and Wigan. She lives in Brighton and is working on her novel, *36D*.

"**I**sn't that that bloke?"

"What bloke? Where? Oh, Jesus, it is, it's him!"

"Nice shirt." Donna turned back to face the bar, shoulders shaking.

"Did he look like that last time?" Vicky asked. "Surely he can't have looked that bad, or I wouldn't have …? I thought he looked like Steve Bull, last time."

"That was only because he had a Wolves shirt on and a crew cut. Not that Hawaiian nightmare." Donna tried to attract the barman's attention, casually waving a ten pound note.

"Nobody wears shirts like that, not in town, anyway. Someone ought to tell him."

Donna raised her eyebrows. "You, you mean? Stop staring, they'll see you."

"Too late. That beanpole one has spotted you. The one you called a lanky streak of piss, to his face. Shall we go over?"

"Vicky, leave it out, I want another drink," Donna complained, but she allowed herself to be pulled across the room. The DJ cranked the music volume up another notch.

As they approached, the three other blokes huddled closer to the one in the Hawaiian shirt, who had his back to them . "Shit, what was his name? I've forgotten his real name! I kept calling him Steve last time." Vicky tapped him on the shoulder. "Hey, thingy. Steve. Nice shirt."

He turned around. It was hard to read his expression. "What's this all about then?" Vicky asked, taking a corner of the tumultuously coloured material between thumb and forefinger, "trying to blind people, or what?" His mates snickered sheepishly.

"Bloody hell," he said, deadpan. "It's Wonder Woman."

Stung, Vicky said, "I see you lost again this week. Three nil, wasn't it?"

Fragments of their last encounter, in Ritzy's, floated back to her again. The bit where he'd said in her ear, in the middle of a conversation about discriminatory and unsporting referees, "are you a 36D?"

After a missed beat, she'd said, "you first – six inches, right? With a stretchy tape measure."

Leaning closer towards her, so close that she could feel the shiny gold polyester of his shirt against her bare arm, he'd said, "I really want to fuck you."

"Hey, " she said now, "how did you get on with the specky one, after I left?"

"Who?"

"That girl, the one with the glasses and no make-up. The one you tried to chat up after I told you to sod off." 'Sod off' was putting it mildly. She'd emptied her drink over his head and considered following it up with the brown glass bottle.

"Oh, her. I wasn't chatting her up, I was just talking to her." He looked quickly over at his three mates, who were now clustered around Donna, not taking any notice of him. "Look – Vicky, isn't it? I was a bit gone, you know, at Ritzy's. Let me buy you a drink, call it quits."

"Yeah, all right," she said happily, "I'll have a bottle of Sol, thanks."

"Sol," he muttered under his breath on the way to the bar. "For fuck's sake."

Donna was getting bored, wandering around. Vicky had backed the guy in the bad shirt up against the fag machine and had her tongue down his throat. His mates were sitting neatly in the corner talking about the three nil disaster, and she really didn't have the patience to pretend to be interested. She walked out to talk to the doorman.

"All right, Alan?" She sat down on the stone step.

"What's up, then? Mate deserted you, has she?"

"Nah, it's only temporary. She'll get bored of him in a bit, you watch. He's thick as shit – when she stops snogging and starts talking it'll all go wrong again. Nice out here, isn't it?"

"Yeah, not bad, not bad."

The bar was a new hybrid for the town – not a club, but a large bar with a late licence and a small dance floor, situated in an old Regency building with high ceilings and ivy round the outside. The heavy late summer weather made Alan sweat in his suit. Donna had started talking to him last week after he'd chucked Mark out for throwing beer at her.

"So, what happened with Mark, then, when you got home?"

"Don't ask. Let's just say it wasn't pleasant. I've had enough of him for a while; he's gone back to live at his mum's."

"You could do better than him, you know."

Donna looked up from the step, surprised.

"You could, honestly. Go back in there and talk to any bloke – I guarantee you, he'd be thrilled to have someone like you take an interest."

Donna smiled to herself. "Do you really think so? Well, maybe I will, then. Cheers, Alan. See you later." She tried not to swing her hips too obviously as she walked back past him.

Vicky was looking for her when she got back inside. "Oh, my God, what was I thinking? Do you know what that bloke's just said to me?"

"Surprise me."

"He said, 'my car's parked behind Safeway, can I shag you?' *Can I shag you*? I haven't heard that since I was about fifteen. *Tosser.*" Vicky shook her head in disbelief.

"Let's get another drink," Donna said. Her mouth wasn't laughing, but her eyes were.

They stood at the bar, close together, a dark head and a blonde one. Donna's new trousers had not arrived from her catalogue in time, and she was out in the same clothes as last week. Vicky was all in pale grey, with a swingy pewter-coloured pendant, heart-shaped. The song of the summer was playing again. As the guy in front of them at the bar turned round with his drinks, he stared at Vicky's pendant and mouthed along with the song,

"What is love? Baby, don't hurt me, don't hurt me, no more," only he said *"heart me"* instead.

"Excuse *me*," Vicky said tetchily, glaring at him as she pushed into his space at the bar.

"Look, there's Warren."

Vicky looked over to where Donna was pointing. "Oh yeah, he's with Craig Nelson and – oh, God, it can't be …"

"What? Who is it?"

"Surely that's – *no*. I don't believe it. Are they still friends?"

Donna stood on tiptoe. "Aha, Jamie, right?" She grinned. "You should have said. I'd have made Warren bring him out long before now. I forgot you used to like him."

"He looks exactly the same." Even from halfway across the room, the sight of Jamie Chapman made Vicky catch her breath. Standing next to Warren, taller and nearly as skinny, he bent his head to listen to something. Vicky clutched her pendant. She could remember what his hair smelled like. It was still the same colour, warm and golden against Warren's paler wispy blond.

Craig saw them and waved. "Come on," Donna said, turning to pull Vicky, who was standing completely motionless.

They fought their way across the now heaving dance floor. Donna insisted Craig buy them a drink. He moved away, and for a moment, nobody said anything. Donna broke the silence. "You remember Vicky, don't you, Jamie?"

He looked at her. "Vicky. Yeah."

Donna slyly nudged Warren to one side, leaving Vicky and Jamie looking at the floor.

"How are you?" Vicky asked, her words slightly slurred. She wished she hadn't drunk quite so much.

"All right. So, out with Donna again?" His voice was deeper than she remembered.

"Yeah, weird, isn't it? I haven't seen you for such a long time – I was probably about fourteen or fifteen. That's seven years. Mad." Aware that she was babbling, Vicky carried on anyway. She wasn't really nervous, more exhilarated. It seemed somehow right that she should bump into Jamie now, with the comfort of a future in front of her. "I used to have a huge crush on you," she said, looking straight at him, trying to emphasise the 'used to'.

He laughed. "Really?"

"Yeah. There was one night, years ago, we were all in the Moors Park getting pissed on gin and Kia-Ora. Christ only knows where Mark got it from."

Jamie snorted at the mention of Mark.

"I ended up getting off with you, and when it got to eleven and I should have been home, I didn't want to go, because I was with you. So we stayed out and walked up town." Vicky blinked, unnerved to hear herself say 'up town'. She plunged on, "I didn't notice that everyone else had gone home. It was just you, me, Donna and Mark. We walked down Market Street, trying all the car doors – Mark said he'd nick one and take us for a drive, but we had to get into one first. Do you remember now, the three wheeler? The cripple car?"

He nodded, amused. "The flidmobile, wasn't it? Not very p.c. of us."

"I said, 'I'll die if this one's open', and it was! That awful turquoise colour – why are they never red or brown or whatever?"

"It's lucky not even Mark was stupid enough to nick a spastic wagon," Jamie said, moving a little closer to her as the area became even more packed.

"It wasn't because he wasn't stupid enough – he was just confused by the steering stick malarkey. He couldn't drive it."

Jamie laughed again. He was so close, Vicky had to stop herself from leaning over to smell him. He still wore the same type of glasses, with thin, angular silver rims.

Craig returned with the drinks. "Here, Vick." He was about to say something else, but Donna whisked him round by the elbow, so professionally that they didn't notice they were no longer a group, but a couple and a threesome.

Vicky scratched the label on her lager bottle. Craig had bought her Holsten Pils instead of Sol. "Do you still like Prince?" she asked Jamie.

"Prince? I guess so, kind of. Why?"

"You started reciting his lyrics at me, in Winston Churchill Gardens, after the cripple car. We made so much noise, laughing, that a bloke came out of a house and started shouting at us. Mark and Donna ran off in a different direction, and we went into the gardens. '*Touch if you will my stum-ache*'. The rest of it seems to have escaped me, for some reason."

Jamie was shaking his head. "Christ, stop! I must have been a complete wanker. Your memory's too good."

"No, you weren't a wanker," Vicky said seriously. Her slurring was becoming more obvious. "It started to rain, so we walked home down Gloucester Road and you wouldn't shut up – something about *Darling Vicky* instead of *Darling Nikki*. Then we got to my road and saw there was a police car outside. I told you to go, but you wouldn't leave until you'd seen me to my house. You know, I was really impressed when that policewoman opened my front door and said, 'Hello, Jamie'."

He was grinning at her, and she remembered how she'd felt when he kissed her on the wet doorstep and walked off without saying good-bye. The policewoman and her mum had gone on for ages about responsibility and not causing worry, but she'd hardly heard a word.

Vicky had run out of things to say and was relieved when Donna poked her head in between theirs. "Don't look now, but that bloke's coming back."

"Not the Hawaiian Nightmare?"

"Yep. Looks like he's really off his face now, too. Half the buttons on his shirt are undone."

"Who's the Hawaiian Nightmare?" Jamie asked.

"A total cretin," Vicky replied, "I was really stupid, earlier, before you lot got here. Actually, I kissed him, but he's awful." Jamie raised his eyebrows, looking more interested than he had all night.

"I'll get rid of him," Craig interjected, thrusting his chin forward.

"Craig, what is that thing with the chin? Don't be silly," Donna said. She lifted Jamie's left arm and draped it around

Vicky's shoulders. "Right, if he comes over, you're her boyfriend, all right?"

"OK, as long as I'm not going to get my head kicked in," Jamie said, quietly. He tightened his arm slightly and Vicky realised she was forgetting to breathe. She let her breath out as soundlessly as possible.

The steps we are sitting on are solid stone, really cold. Jamie lies back and sniffs the air. "What can I smell, those flowers?" he asks.

"I don't know. Jasmine, maybe, or magnolia. I'm a bit horticulturally challenged."

"Horticulturally challenged! Listen to you," he says. "Where do you get words like that from?" He rolls over onto his stomach and I stick my hand up the back of his shirt. He feels quite bony.

"What do you do for a living these days?" I ask. I've told him about Germany, made him promise that he won't tell Donna.

"I lump glass around," he says into the stone step.

"Oh." I don't quite know what he means.

"At the window factory. Big sheets of it, for cutting."

He seems too skinny for that kind of a job. I worked in a window factory once, for a day. The shearing, grinding noises of the frame machines almost deafened me, and I couldn't stand to go back the next day and talk to the girl who'd told me about her three abortions. She couldn't have been more than seventeen.

"Don't you want to do something else?" I ask after a pause. "You're so bright." There is no way I can say that without sounding patronising, but he doesn't seem to mind.

"I'd like to, yeah, of course. I'd like to be a surveyor, or an architect."

"So why don't you do something about it? You're only, what, twenty-four? That's not too late, it's never too late. You could go to college, get some qualifications."

He shifts round onto his back again, pulls me towards him and kisses me. Back in the bar, when he finally bent his face down to mine and our lips met, I thought for a disgraceful moment that I was going to do something unforgivable, like faint. At an animal level, he is my most perfect human. The smell of his hair, his neck; it's sublime. If humans really do choose each other by smell, as they claim in those pheromone adverts, then he is my chemical other half. Blindfolded in a room full of people, I would choose him every time.

Across the street, the outer door of the bar opens and music blurts out into the street. It sounds like *'What is Love?'* again. "Perhaps we should go back in," I say. "Donna'll be looking for me and it is rather uncouth to be sprawled all over the Town Hall steps like this."

"No, don't go in," Jamie says. "Not yet, anyway. It's so nice out here; we've got drinks – leave it a bit. You'll probably start to feel sick again if we go in now. Donna won't mind, she's with that bloke."

It's true; she is. The lanky streak of piss. "Bless her," I say.

Donna comes out before we think about going in again. The lanky streak of piss, whose name is Nigel, can't seem to take his mouth away from her neck. "What are you doing?" she asks. "Get off her, Jamie, it's unseemly. I know you've got your trousers on, but really! People come to the Town Hall to listen to Mozart – have you no respect?" Nigel seems to have bought her a lot of drinks. She's as unsteady on her feet as I would be if I stood up, and talking very carefully. "It's a pity that the geer bar … beer gardens are now closed."

Many years ago, she and I were benignly served a round there, consisting of five pints of Grolsch, two Pernod and blacks and a pint of snakebite, whilst both wearing our school uniform, mine navy, hers grey. This town is full of our history.

"What time is it?" I ask.

"Half-one. Here." There's a jangle as she tosses her keys to me. "Going back with Nigel for a coffee. See you in the morning. *Condoms in the bedside cabinet, top drawer,*" she adds in a stage whisper. *"Have fun!"* They walk off towards the Promenade, Nigel still attached to her neck as they go. I hear Jamie chuckle in the darkness.

"Hey, hang on. Won't be a minute, Jamie." I scramble up and run after them. "Excuse us a moment, " I say to Nigel, prising

Donna away from him. "What's going on? Are you sure you'll be OK? We don't know this bloke at all."

She says disjointedly, "Noo, it's only, Nigel, see. No sweat. Mark is back at his mum's, Danni's with my mum, no need to worry. Me an' Nigel – coffee, bed. Be with you in the morning. You know where everything is; clean nighties in the airing cupboard. Jamie Chapman, indeed. *Vicky!*" She punches me lightly in the side, links arms with Nigel and strolls off, waving grandly. I walk slowly back to Jamie, who is sprawled artistically over three steps.

"Help me up," he pleads. "Too much beer."

I grasp his hand and pull him up. I got up too quickly myself and my head is rushing. We stand swaying together for a moment. For the first time tonight, I don't know what to say.

Jamie strokes my hair and murmurs into my ear, "So, coffee at Donna's then?"

We take a taxi home. It has electric windows and we annoy the driver by zipping them up and down all the way there. Donna's bunch of keys is huge and it takes ages to select the right combination to open the door. Inside, I go to turn the lights on, but Jamie stops me. "No, look, it's moonlight. If we just open the curtains, it'll be much nicer."

I make a cup of tea in the silent, bare kitchen and return to Jamie on the sofa. We sit side by side for a moment, sipping. The moonlight streaks in through the patio doors, giving all the colours in the room a washed-out look. I wonder what I look like now – it's more than three hours since my last make-up adjustment.

We both start to speak at once, and stop, laughing. The tea has revived us. Jamie pushes me down into the sofa cushions and we lie full length, twined together.

"Look at the size of that TV," he says suddenly.

"What?" I don't understand. "What about the TV?"

"It's *tiny*. The TV in my bedroom is bigger than that."

"Yeah, well, you still live with your mum," I almost snap, "and you've got a job. Don't be sarky."

"Can I have another cup of tea?" he asks.

"There's no more milk for tea," I have to reply. I can feel him holding in a sigh. "Do you want some squash?"

When I come back, he puts the squash down immediately and drags me onto the sofa again. He reaches around my back with one arm and eases my bra undone, gently and expertly. Warren told me earlier that Jamie hasn't been with anyone since he split up with his last girlfriend nearly three years ago. Warren is too dense to lie efficiently, so it must be true. Jamie's hands are unhurried and sure, but his breathing is all over the place. So is mine. He circles my left nipple with his finger and I arch my back, but then I want the loo, and my concentration goes. Eventually, I am surprised to find that I feel sleepy.

"Jamie?" I whisper, "I don't know about you, but I think I should go to bed."

We go upstairs and I escape into the bathroom, hazy now from all the alcohol I've drunk. I look in the mirror – I look like shit, but Donna only has electrifyingly yellow *Zest* soap and I daren't wash my face with that in case I wake up with a rash. I peel off my clothes and pull out a nightdress from the airing cupboard. It's a horrible T-shirt one with a cartoon character on the front that I've never heard of, but it smells of muted Lenor and it's soft. Hesitating only slightly, I leave my knickers on.

In the bedroom, Jamie has stripped to his boxer shorts and is sitting up in bed with one of my shoes in his hand. "Small feet," he says tiredly, squinting up at me. He's taken his glasses off, I notice with a jolt. He looks unsettlingly different, his face somehow vaguer, but he has a nice, taut chest. I turn the light out and get into bed.

We lie for a moment in silence, the darkness welcome. I feel completely spent. I try to say goodnight, but my throat is so dry that nothing comes out. Propping myself on one elbow, I take a sip of water. When I lie back down, Jamie reaches for me, pulling me close. The shock of our skin together for the first time wakes me up slightly, and he bites my bottom lip gently as we kiss which sends shivers down my spine, but I still really want to go to sleep. He rolls on top of me. I lie limply for a while as my head begins to spin unpleasantly.

"Where did Donna say the condoms were?" Jamie whispers. His cock has been hard on and off all night, I've been caressing and thrusting, and I can't think of anything viable to say now.

"Um, bedside cabinet, top drawer."

I can hear him scrabbling around. It almost sounds half-hearted; he's not making much noise. "Can't find any," he says, turning back to me.

I find myself reaching over him, searching with both hands through the drawer, even as my mind is saying, *no, stop, turn over, go to sleep*. One hand closes on a small packet, a hard oval ridge inside. "Here's one," I say, and pass it to him before I can stop myself.

He reaches up my nightie and strokes my breasts with the back of his hand. I make a final attempt to beat the alcohol-induced fug and let out a gentle moan, but realistically, it's too late. I think Jamie knows that too. He's obviously an imaginative lover, but using the back of his hand is his last original effort. From then on, he is just going through the motions; I am as responsive as an ironing board and only marginally less rigid. A quick feel, knickers gently eased off, a bit of vaginal fumbling, assume missionary position, ingress, then a small revival as I manage to clasp my legs around his back, which quickly ebbs. In, out, in, out, and with every fading thrust, I think, *I've blown it, I've blown it*.

I awake with a jump, furiously hot and frightened. "The ceiling's on fire," I mutter and lash out, thumping Jamie on the back.

"What?" He is awake instantly. "What's the matter?"

"Ceiling's on fire," I say again, even though by now I'm pretty sure it was a dream. "Downstairs, we left the light on and the ceiling is on fire."

He gets out of bed without saying anything else and goes downstairs. It is still quite dark. I push the duvet off to cool myself down.

Jamie comes back a minute later with a tall glass of water. "Nothing there, don't worry. You were just dreaming. Go back to sleep, it's not even six o'clock yet." He passes the water to me;

I take a long drink and slump back, too bleary to speak. The bed creaks as Jamie gets back in.

"Good night," he says. We turn away from each other to go to sleep, not touching.

I wake up again at nine and lie dazed for a moment, staring with half-closed eyes at the harsh red numerals on Donna's digital clock. As soon as I move my head, it begins to thump. Inching myself up the pillow slightly, I try to open my eyes properly, but they are prickly with stale mascara. I look round gingerly and see Jamie's golden head on the pillow next to me, his glasses on the bedside table. Pausing to retrieve my knickers from where they landed over the head of a scary, white-faced, clown doll last night, I stumble towards the bathroom.

After washing my face with the sharp *Zest* soap, I search Donna's bathroom cabinet for moisturiser and paracetamol. I find a bottle of Johnson's Baby Lotion and smooth some on my sore face. It is pink and balmy, but there are no paracetamol, only some of Dannielle's Junior Disprin. Too groggy to read the dosage, I dissolve six in a glass of water and hope they don't upset my stomach, which is currently pleasingly stable. Finding a stray Lemsip sachet, I take that too, for good measure, mixing it with lukewarm tap water. Finally, I clean my teeth with Dannielle's Mr Happy toothbrush, mentally promising to buy her a new one. The two big toothbrushes make me sad, with their pitifully splayed bristles. I return to the bedroom, having successfully managed to avoid looking at myself in the mirror the whole time. I'm scared that I might look like the white-faced clown.

The painkillers kick in quite quickly, abating the headache, but all the water I have drunk sends the residual alcohol coursing through my system again and I feel dizzy. I lie quietly until it passes, listening to Jamie's tranquil breathing. I don't want to think about last night, not the last bit, anyway.

Somewhere close outside a police siren pulsates along the road and Jamie wakes up.

DAMON THOMAS MULLINS

Revising Loss

Damon Thomas Mullins was born in Columbus, Ohio in 1976.

He graduated from Wittenburg University in Springfield, Ohio, in English Literature, majoring in Creative Writing with a minor in Political Science. He believes that his writing stems from the vibe of the Hip-Hop Culture.

Scorched Crops

He staggers past the preacher's house, after almost blacking out
like an old light bulb at the town bar. And the drunken farmer
is in a tremble, his rumbling thoughts are surrounded
by his scorched crops.

At the pastor's window, he stumbles to a halt,
looks in through the crack of the curtains, notices.
The sun never shines into his window so brilliant
and delicate like it does on the preacher's glowing soul.

He sees the pastor with his Bible and halo,
around the dinner table in prayer, with Mary Jo,
little Andy, and Sue Ann. He curses God's name,
leaks by the doormat like an old, dripping faucet.

After the stench pours with a crisp satisfaction in the grass,
he leaves with his finger up to the sun, heads up the road
to his broken down farmhouse to dowse himself with grain alcohol,
unfold his black tongue, arouse the crows. He wants them
to attack the unfair sky until it falls.

The Dark Blue Night

My, my, my,
his impact here
has been insignificant,
seems small as an ant.

Oh, the dark blue night.
The sky's wingspan is over
his face like a quiet night bird,
he can almost caress the beak.

His sombre eyes are up like astronauts,
up through the twinkling spectacle,
up through to spying heavens.

He reaches up with his hand,
sadly grasps the cold air illusion
like a magician.

He has faith
in the gate-keeper,
knows
He is watching,

rocking time away in his wicker chair,
jingling a ring of keys,
a still and unready inception.

Unable to escape
the dark, blue ego
he reaches up,
but the sky recedes.

Lynched

He is waving goodbye to us.
Rubs his arms together like two branches on fire.

He is in the middle of scattering flames;
Palms are browning, wrists snapping, lips silent.

He is waiting to break in full bark, waiting
for skin to tear and the smell of flesh to be over.

The crackling is sparkling on the tip of his tongue.
Under the fierce sun, he will shrivel up

like a vineless blackberry ripped from the spine,
so kiss him goodbye.

He is over Fahrenheit now. Lava is blazing over him.
He is becoming like syrup, pouring into a new death.

In a heavy heat of the Deep South,
his sweet soul is becoming black smoke.

Escaping Slavery

Once upon a time a slave's bones
were tired like soil in the winter.
He was thirsty, watching the birds
migrate, slowly, sadly with air
in their dark hairs.

If only he could fly to the promised land.
Drink milk, honey, berries, and bread.
If only he could touch the rays
of ending summer sun.
He could see them from afar,
shimmering off the lake.

As his thoughts drank from the long landscape,
he felt someone at his shoulder,
it was his guardian angel,
and she whispered.

Drink, slave, drink,

and as she appeared,
his master appeared.
He held a bucket of cool water,
and he said,

Drink, slave, drink.

But if he could only fly to the promised land.
He made a covenant. Next summer
he would work more steadily,
be done with work early,
then lie in the afternoon grass,
dreaming clouds were ships with wings,
or legs without chains.

Fenced In

The wife's smirk is content.
She is going through the circular motions,
squeezing the sponge, knives and forks,
washing the dirty dishes left over from dinner,
wipes her hands on her apron, then she notices.

There is a small window above the sink, has no bars.
She looks over her shoulder; her husband is not present.
A glimpse out the small window at the waist-high fence,
she notices.

There is a flimsy plant. It's gangling over the iron gate,
wanting to grow into the open space
and snail trails are surrounding, preventing an escape;
right there where dead fruits, dry roots and vegetables lay.

The separation of the man-of-the-house snail
and the blue-in-the-face,
sunless plant is her only chance. See.
The sly snail is slowly sucking the plant of breath.

It is barely surviving, struggling to avoid the rake,
lunging between holes in the fence,
leaving the estate.

Mary

The black soul singer once had a cherry heart.
She was chasing a dragon, of cloudy mind,
caught in a blizzard of used needles, black-eyed.
Mary's lover pusher pimp, a beast of all animals,
found her gigs, fed her ribs, held her hips
took dips in her pockets for snow white powder.

Dream-on, Mary, he said. Ruthless, toothless,
grabbed her smoothly by the wrists,
he was a ghetto street pharmacist;
thugged-out, drugged-out
with fat, bald, bearded henchmen.

Mary was strung-out like a cat hung on a telephone wire.
She got flexed-on, slept-on, slapped around.
After years of rotting underneath a cut-throat,
she cut his throat. She was free.
A black star outcast in the dark streets.
She sang on at the inner-city night-clubs,
oh, what a pity, the crowd got joy,
her sweet voice.

Kathy

Her nickname, Kitty, made Kathy feel
she was to play the role of the cotton candy actress,
a boy-crazy game. Her unfortunate fame came
when handsome Randy pulled to the curb
in rowdy Rodney's blue convertible Sunbird,
with his profile out the window,
gracing the suburbs.

That night she clawed at the leather interior
like a pent-up cat on the loose.
She terrifically keyed the car the next.
Revenge. They spread rat tales about sex.
Claimed to prevail in taking a voyage to her depths.
Which they maintained to pervertedly penetrate,
pulverising her to a pulp.

One gulp from chin to throat and nothing was left of her.
After the poor actress performed for a pretend director,
producer, and the red light of the camera.
Its open eye was as solid as their seducing lies;
both stayed focused for the records,
confirmed their rat tales to death.

Poor Kathy took a swan dive off a high cliff,
landed smack down, spot-on like a kiss.
All for handsome Randy's dandy rambling,
and rowdy Rodney's easy way of handling things.

What the Groom and Bridesmaid did before the Wedding

Before the two o'clock tying of the knot,
just when the twelve o'clock sun shone like a fat boiled egg
in an auburn sky, an eager bridesmaid stood upright
by the church entrance.

When the wedding party passed
in yellow dresses and blue blazers,
she turned her head away
uninvolved in the proud parade.

A taxi pulled up, paused, let out a passenger, then passed.
A handsome gentle-like-man posed in elegant position
with a smirk painted on his face like a sinful saint.

He wore silver cufflinks, a mocking black tuxedo,
and stood with an imposter's posture, straight up.
She restrained her moans, the weight of her thighs heavy,
her stiff eyes burning silent with the violent sun.

He signalled from across the busy street. Well into his spell,
she slightly wiggled her hips to shake off hell, returned
the signal, which was a proficient pass of sick rapport,

a ritual in perverted performance.
After fiendish exhales, broken vows were taken;
dirty wedding bells were ringing.

They even danced together at the reception,
smiling into each other's vicious, drunken,
eyes of deception.

Pretending to be my Tree

Do you lie, she asked?
Sometimes, I replied.

You don't lie to me, do you?
No, I am not a liar,
I replied as I placed the book,
Pinnocchio,
back on the shelf.

Water is what I wanted for our tree,
like lady gardener had given as a gift to my last love affair's needs.
It was spring,
I longed for her water in my soil,

so I said;

a lady once told me a tale
where lying led to happiness.
Do you lie, I asked her?
Sometimes, she replied,
but I am not a liar.

Then what is a liar?
Is it someone who pretends like a chameleon is a tree,
but can't grow leaves?

Yes, I guess, she said.

Well, why lie about our lives,
they're already beautiful within.

Sunlight is what I wanted her to give me,
for our tree.
like lady gardener had given as a gift to my last love affair's needs.
It was spring, I longed for her to shine on my leaves.

Grief and Misunderstandings

Why do they bury you in this ground?
Don't they know you were born of mom,
not dirt? Isn't this disrespectful to her?
Why do they put that stone by your head?
Don't they know you slept on soft pillows?

Everyone at the funeral is like the dog.
Carrying flowers, digging up earth to hide bones,
in a sweet dream. Surely you'll have nightmares,
but sweet dreams, anyway, brother.

You know the old people, the liars,
they cut words on the stones,
it read Rest-in-Peace.
Don't they know that you died
on a Saturday morning during cartoons,
after only living fifteen years?

You were so ugly when you left us.
But even if you eat worms for the rest of your days,
I still think you were, as mom says, handsome.
Well, try to get some sleep now;
pray that I don't leave mom,
like you left her.

from *Fancydancing with Elvis*

Tiffany Murray grew up on the border of The Forest of Dean. Her first job was as roadie for her father as he toured Forest pubs with a guitar and black cowboy boots. She has since worked as a journalist, Ph.D. student and dog-walker in New York, where she lived for six years. She has now returned to The Forest, the setting for *Fancydancing with Elvis*, her first novel.

Harry Morgan was cradled in a dip of the forest floor: his hands shut tight in his armpits; the large dog curled small into his stomach; the wool blanket over them both. The ground, soft with moss, was sheltered beneath the high knots of pinetrees.

Samson licked his cheek, the lurcher's tongue warming his bristled skin. Harry stretched and lay flat. The plastic sheet beneath him crackled and he opened his eyes to the moving forest. It was still quite dark, early morning, but he soon saw through the grey light.

There was a rush of wind, a pair of crows jumped from the high needle branches, letting out retching cries. Harry stared up into the creak of trees and shivered. *Someone's walking over my grave*, he thought, feeling the touch of hot water. *Someone's walking over my grave*. His eyes closed to the sound of wood giving.

"Someone's dancing on your grave, Harry, I can hear them!" Irene says this giggling, a girl again.

She puts her small red head to the ground, pigtails heavy on the weak grass, freckled limbs sticking out from mam's old gingham dress. *"Quick! Come and listen!"* she cries and he is there; her big brother in short trousers. He goes down on all fours, and laughs as she jumps on his back:

"Ha, ha! I am, I'm the one who's dancing on your grave, ha, ha!"

Lying there in the morning cold, Harry could almost feel her weight, small and comforting.

He had to wake, and sat up; the air chilling as he rose. He stood and shook his huge body, then, jumping from one foot to the other, hugged himself. *Getting too old for this, nearly fifty, not a boy no more.* Under the blanket, Samson shivered.

Feeling a flush of body heat Harry was still; blank and ragged as a just-woken child. He looked out at the trees; sap stained their trunks like whitewash, he breathed in the potent scent. When they had first cut the oaks and planted pines, he called them fishbone trees; with their parallel rungs of lower bare branches they reminded him of fish backs stuck in the earth. They weren't real at all.

The ground around him was lush; bright club moss covering everything from fallen, rotted trunks to old boots and crisp packets. Harry had always thought that this was what the seabed must be like, so still and permanent. As a boy he had loved pretending to be one of those weighted divers, the men with the big bubble heads he'd seen in picture books. He had played that game for hours, slow-motion moving under the heavy silence of trees, lurching stiff as Frankenstein's monster, his boots filled with stones, off to plunder the wrecks of felled pines.

Nowadays, as he lay in the forest at night, Harry sometimes had bad dreams; he'd feel the moss spreading over his own body, see his cheeks, mould-stained, vegetal, and wake with the blanket over his face.

In the distance he noticed movement and crouched. Resting his arms on the lip of the hole he peered into the mist of dawn light, watching shadows pass slowly, methodically, through the lines of deep red trunks. They were deer; four females and their prickets, two black, the others dappled. Samson stuck his snout out from under the blanket; the wind picked up the dog's scent and one doe froze, sounding her strange whittling alarm; above them a wood pigeon slapped into flight. The deer ran back into the thick plantation.

"Right, boy?" said Harry, laughing, and stepped out of his shelter. Samson yawned, arched his back and shook himself, sniffing the air. Harry grabbed the dead rabbits hung from the upper branch of a pine, fixed them to his belt, and fastened his coat over them to hide the catch.

They walked from the darkness of trees to one of the network of tracks that patterned the forest. Harry squinted in the sudden light; the air was colder; the ground still covered in a film of frost, like cellophane.

At the edge of the pineforest, Harry noticed fresh wood shavings littering the trail. The Forestry Commission were felling quick-growing Douglas Firs. Two marker trees cordoned off the area; a steel wire cutting into them had made their growth bulge around the tourniquet, giving them the shape of corseted women. Logs were piled high, ready for the morning lorries and the saw mill; yellow signs warned *DANGER!* and bright orange hard hats lay on the ground. Men would be here soon. Harry looked up to see the wasteland where trees had stood. The ground was black with oil from machines. It didn't worry him; the forest was constant, as soon as it was razed it would grow again, smothering everything. Harry had faith in this permanence. He walked on, boots sucked by mud.

Trees diminished, the ground leveled off and he turned onto the lane. It was nice to have solid ground beneath him, he liked the thud of his boots on the uneven tarmac. Magpies hopped tail-up in the fields either side of him, he counted; *one, sorrow; two, joy; three, girl; four, boy; five…* before they flew up into the trees, heavy in the air.

He felt a brief lick of rain and looked out over the white meadows; traces of red, late-dawn light still poured over them. As he passed, Harry saw three high-staked bonfires, each with a sock-stuffed Guy Fawkes at the top, waiting for darkness. He knew today's date, but had tried to ignore this irritation. He spat on the ground and moved on, Samson keeping exactly in step.

Following the last twist of the road he reached the Industrial Estate and the outskirts of Lydford. He watched his shadow spread out in front of him, extra tall in the winter sun now catching the valley. Suddenly a white Ford Cortina raced round the bend, blaring its horn, forcing him into the verge.

"Get outa the bloody road Morgan!"

"Getoutafit!"

Harry recognised the voices; Bert and Billy Pritchard. He paused, called Samson to heel and carried on to the waking town.

Mavis Lewis unbolted the shop door, her grey hair still in rollers. Scissors in hand, she bent down to cut the string holding the newspapers together. Her back twinged. *Bloody van*, she thought, cursing the new delivery service. Time was when the paperman would knock and carry these bundles right into her shop, giving her a nice *Mornin' Missus!* Not now, she had to kneel in the cold and carry them in small piles, she couldn't manage the whole lot.

The Daily Mirror was first, a great thickness of copies right on the counter, then it was *The Sun* and back out into the cold for *The Forester* and a few copies of *The Times* for tourists. She pressed her winged NHS glasses into the bridge of her nose, just to make out the headlines; some gossip about that Thorpe man again, bloody rubbish all of it. Mavis turned back, locked her door and got ready for the morning.

She moved through her cluttered shop like a wind up toy, busying herself with nothing. Her shelves were stocked with everything ever needed during the war years and since; from darning needles and plastic rain caps to a quarter of rosy apples and some pear drops please. Hoarded Campbell's Soup tins and Camp Coffee bottles sat next to a large jar full of Bay City Rollers and Marc Bolan pin-badges. Her exclusive range of sewing patterns offering Margaret Lockwood evening dresses were displayed next to *The Beano*, and extra supplies of sparklers for those last minute buys. Mavis Lewis's shop smelled of damp and rat poison.

Harry pressed his warm forehead against her cold window. It would be perfect for mam. The bottle was oval, cut glass. A silver-plated stopper ballooned from its neck in the shape of a lumpy camel. It was for her lavender scent. He usually bought her Yardley, from Boots The Chemists in Berryfield – a purple box with plastic wrapping and a little-bo-peep girl on the front – but, *a change is as good as a rest*. He preferred the look of the camel.

The pane steamed up with his breath. Mavis was getting impatient. That Harold was marking her windows, his too-heavy head pressing his flesh white against the glass. She came out from the counter, her nylon shop-coat snagging on its corner. "Bloody man!" she muttered, walking to him. Her wedding ring sounded a hard rap as she knocked on the pane. Harry jumped back and reddened, pointing at the bottle.

In his bulging wax coat, with his huge muddy boots and that dog, Mavis found him a great disappointment. He had been such an angelic boy, all those years ago, in between the wars, and hadn't she helped poor Rose Morgan through that birth, him such a big baby. Later, she had even tried to help him with his reading, though it never did any good. Looking at him now, a man who should have grown-up children of his own she felt frustration, and a little love. Mavis unbolted her door.

"It's too early Harold," she said, standing on her threshold. Harry didn't move. "Well, come in if you're going to, mind you wipe your feet and you can keep that bloody dog out too."

The entrance bell rang as the door shut. Harry stood on the spot, dragging the soles of his boots across her tan-brush mat. He coughed and decided to stay put.

Secure behind her counter, Mavis opened her compact and applied her morning face, all powder and lipstick. "Well, what is it catches your fancy then? Haven't seen you for a while. Your mother comes in to see me regular mind."

Harry was hot in the shop. He hadn't been in here for years, not since mam was last sick. He looked around at the high-stacked shelves, cluttered with his boyhood. Rows of glass jars reminded him of sweet runs with Irene, when he first started work in the pit and had money to spend. That was all dead now. He turned back to the window, pointing to the bottle. "You think mam'll like it?" he asked.

Mavis snapped her compact shut and stared at him. She had hoped it wasn't a purchase, last time she got a brace of over high pheasant and a nostril-bleeding rabbit dripping on her carpet. "Is it Rose's birthday Harold?" she said, knowing the answer.

"Aye."

"That's a nice thing for a man to buy for his mam, isn't it Harold?"

"Reckon."

She laughed and walked towards him. As she neared Harry she listened to his heavy breathing and felt the air warm around him; he smelled of healthy sweat. Mavis rearranged the faded envelope of a dress-pattern on the magazine rack; "It's three pounds. No exchanges."

Harry reached in his coat pocket. Opening his hand he offered various crumpled one-pound notes. Mavis carefully picked out three, her nails catching on his rough palms. "Do you want it wrapped?" she asked, brushing past him.

"Aye."

She picked up the bottle and, returning to her counter, rolled it up in a white paper bag. "Now you give my regards to your mam, tell her to visit." She walked back to him and held out the gift.

"Right," said Harry, looking down at her.

Mavis felt herself blushing beneath her powder. She looked away, then at her hands; she noticed how her gold band cut into the flesh of her wedding finger. She coughed and turned to the baby-ware section, the piles of woolen jackets and booties all her own work. Mavis heard the bell ring above the doorframe. Harold was gone.

The small house had warmed in his absence. Mam had piled coal high on the fire. In the back kitchen he untied the stiff rabbits, slamming them hard on the draining board, and shuffled into the front room. As soon as he sat, Harry took off his large boots and put them on the newspaper already laid out.

Mam had left breakfast for him, warming on the shelf at the back of the cast-iron range. She would be in church now; an early morning service and a visit with flowers for Father and Jamie in the churchyard. Harry wolfed his food, cleaning his plate with a doorstep of white bread. When he had finished he walked out into the back garden, still in his socks.

Samson's food was in the shed. Harry ladled it out into a deep enamel bowl and fed him. He was tired and stared out at the garden, eyes half-open. With mam's fallow vegetable patch, his few rotting rabbit hutches, the hundreds of empty jars lined up against the stone wall, it was a mess. He walked across the grass, the damp coming through his socks, and thought of Irene. Samson trotted past his master and back into the house. Harry stood there for a moment, then followed the dog inside.

Rose Morgan sat on the edge of her bed, staring down at her boy. The light outside was fading, she had had a long day, what with the church and a trip to Gloucester with the ladies as a special treat. Seventy-four and at last she was beginning to feel old. It was a relief.

She leant over and touched his hair. Greasy. Such a good-looking boy and he really should care for himself. His big hand lay on top of her quilt. She took it in hers, feeling its weight.

"Harold? Harold? Tea's ready."

Harry woke, trained to respond to that voice; "Mam."

"Come on now, it's getting cold. Then it's a bath and a shave."

He felt happy, with a full belly and a clean back, after all mam's scrubbing. *I may be old but I can still give it a bit of elbow grease*, she said, leaning over the soapy water, her hands plunging in, her apron wet through. His face was smooth, child-like now. Standing in her bedroom, dressed in his best and only suit, he crouched to see his reflection in the dressing table mirror.

Downstairs Rose was making herself look pretty, just a little lipstick and blue-creme eyeshadow.

"You coming down boy?"

"Right mam," Harry yelled, combing his wet hair, getting the parting crooked. He jumped down the high squat stairs, landing heavy on the flag stones.

"Now, don't you look smart. See, if you only make a bit of effort you look like a right Prince."

"Ah, mam! Don't!" He blushed as his mother giggled.

Harry took her hand and they moved towards the parlour. The generator was switched off, the corridor in darkness as Rose turned the key. It was stiff, but her strong hands managed it. They walked in. The room was cold and smelled of mothballs. Harry struck a match and lit one of the Duplex Oilamps.

He twisted the cogwheel and the wick rose, bringing oil with it. The flickering light intensified, revealing a room filled with photographs. Some were framed, others unframed; they hung on every bit of wall space, stuck in with tin-tacks or nails, covering the long-faded lily wallpaper. Black and white and colour were also propped up on occasional tables, but most lay stacked on the floor; different coloured ribbons holding them together. This was Rose's gallery; these people her treasures. She had started her collection as a girl in service during the first war, stealing photographs from her Welsh employers. She had had to wait until after the second war for a camera of her own. Now her life was banked up in these piles of known and unknown faces; each era colour coded with precious strips of silk.

Apart from these embellishments and two bouquets of plastic flowers from Jamie and Father's funeral, the parlour was almost empty.

Rose walked around the room, her pinched hands trailing along the dusty tops of her massed pictures, stopping only to finger a yellowed newspaper clipping, framed and hung above the blackened mantelpiece. It read: "Pit Explosion in Dean: Many Dead." She was proud of this; it had been second page in *The Express*, all those years ago. After a moment she moved away from the words. This was her's and Harold's night, nobody else's.

Harry stood at the drinks cabinet, pouring out a sweet sherry. The cap was sticky with liquor. "Here you go mam, happy birthday."

Rose drank and Harry turned back to help himself to a little of Father's whiskey, still unfinished.

He was trying not to look up. He knew she was there, she always had been. She was a baby, smiling down, with one tooth and a cow-lick curl. Next to this she was a girl, grinning with the rest of her class; thick pigtails and a huge gap instead of front teeth. Then the photographs changed; Irene grew up fast. She had been so little for so long, it was a shock. Harry walked over to one of the display tables pressed up to the wall and there she was, the new Irene in one colour photograph; her red pigtails manipulated into a bee-hive of hair; her too-big dresses now tight belted slips; her fat feet sucked into high, pointed shoes. Mam had called her nothing but a little tart.

He reached out to touch the technicolor picture. He thought it beautiful. His face flushed, *must be the whiskey*. Harry hadn't seen Irene for eleven years. Cards came from Redditch at Christmas, mam hid them, there was nothing else.

"Who a' you looking at, Harold?"

He turned to face her; "Nothing mam."

"Don't go upsetting me, now."

Harry took another sip of whiskey.

"Careful," said Rose, "drinks is bad for your head."

There was silence as they gazed at one another, then a sudden blast of fireworks came up from the valley, followed by distant screams. It was past seven and Guy Fawkes night had begun on Lydford Common.

Harry walked to a polished wood box in the corner, crouched, and began to wind the handle. "It's your day mother, what d'you fancy, eh?"

Rose laughed; "Well, how's about a little Foxtrot? But you be careful mind, I ent young no more!"

He chose her favourite. It was no surprise, they had it every year. He opened the lid of the box and, fingering only the middle and edges of the 78, trying not to touch its precious grooves, Harry took the record from its brown paper bag and slotted it onto the green felt turntable. He chose a sharper needle from the little pile in the machine, unscrewing the old one and letting it drop into his palm. Looking up at the underside of the lid, he traced the picture with his finger; he loved the Jack Russell sat up against that funnel, with those magic words – *His Master's Voice*. As he lifted the fat, silver arm up and across, the mechanism clicked and the record spun. Harry placed the needle on the thick, black carbon and waited for the crackle to drown the distant, ugly bangs.

There was a rush of noise from the machine, the scream of a muted trumpet. Mam laughed. Harry stood, opened his arms and walked towards her. "Care for this dance?" he asked, grabbing her pliable side in one hand, her fingers in the other. As

Harry spun Rose around the parlour, her slippered feet dragged on the stone-slab floor.

He was very good, Rose had taught him from a boy. As they turned, Harry leading, that strange falsetto voice came, singing:

By the light of the Silvery Moon!
I want to swoon, with my honey I'll croon love's tune

Harry nestled into his mother, bending his body over. He loved the touch of her clothes, always thrilled by their synthetic softness. He relaxed into the dance, surrounded by her fading gallery, and forgot everything apart from this touch. There was nothing else and he was a boy again. It was a Holy Day and he was leaning into her; shivering even in summer in Little Dean Primitive Methodist Chapel. The choir sang 'Hear the Pennies Dropping', although they never did and his elbow was lodged between the third and fourth roll of her fat, his chin buried into the side of her man-made bosom, smelling of Lux flakes and lavender.

As he danced with her, the room spinning along with the old record, he snuffled his face down into her hair, lost in its sweet taste.

The fireworks had frightened his quarry underground, or deep into the warm of Lydford Wood's thickets. The only noise was Harry's footsteps, shuffling through wide-spanned sycamore leaves. The rhythmical sound soothed him as he wandered in the early morning night, aimless, his traps empty.

He leant against a beech trunk and took out his tobacco pouch. Sucking smoke, he watched the glow of the roll-up recede and crouched, his back flat against the smooth, grey bark.

An odd cry came from the direction of the forest. Harry didn't move. It would be kids from the town, messing about. It sounded again, high-pitched, animal. Samson cocked his head and whined. Harry paused, waiting for a repeat, then stood and turned leisurely up through the dry crack of fern. There was little else to do but follow the mysteries of the night.

They climbed over the stile into Copse Meadow, casting a deformed shadow across the grass, and walked on towards the first line of conifers.

"Over boy," he whispered, and Samson leapt across the jump strand of the forest fence.

Inside Harry was still, eyes temporarily blind, acclimatising to the pitch dark of tight-planted trees. He stopped breathing, to listen, then bent low to pass under the tickling arms of a spruce, its branches scaled like lizards' legs.

The ground was sponge, littered with browning needles, shattered dead wood and rusting cans. The squealing wasn't far. Harry moved through the rows of pines towards the sound, then stopped. In one of the dips of the ground, he saw movement.

"Down!" he hissed and Samson shot to the floor.

Harry peered through the black, his eyes clearer. He made out a small creature, screeching now with the human scent so close. He lay on his stomach and edged slowly towards the form, pulling himself along on the point of his elbows. At his approach the animal began to yowl, mad as a feral cat. Harry stopped, confused; then he began to laugh, low and quiet. The forest had tricked him again. He sat up.

"Hello there! Was the matter with you eh?" Harry reached out to a small dog and felt a snare caught around its front paw.

"We'll have to fix you up pup, wun we?" he said, touching the animal's wet cut to loosen the wire. He took off his scarf and wrapped it around the dog's leg. It whined, chewing at his hand with sharp puppy teeth. "There now!" he said

Lifting the animal up Harry noticed cloth covering its back-legs and belly. The pup licked his face, and he saw something dangling from its collar. He put the dog back on the ground, and leant forward to pull the wooden peg of the snare from the earth.

As he did this, he felt a sudden though slight weight on his shoulder. There was a sound like a growl, something gripped his neck and his eyes went blind. Grabbing the warm blinkers covering his sight, he yanked the offending object off his back and down with a hollow thump on the forest floor.

There was a noise, a sharp release of air like a punctured tyre. Harry moved quickly, climbing on top of the thing. He pinned its lower half down with his knees, holding on to what felt like shoulders. *Could be one of the keeper's lads, someone looking to get me.*

He looked down and saw a small face, a gaping mouth and fit-to-burst eyes. It was a girl. Unable to match this with what he had expected Harry didn't move, then, hearing a wheeze, he leapt off.

He was still, his arms hanging limp at his sides. The rasping noise filled the air; above him, branches swayed. Harry gazed at the dusty floor and noticed flecks of white. They were feathers, probably a wood pigeon got by a fox; their small shafts were wet, the white barbs darkly matted. He reached out to touch one and the gasping stopped.

The girl was only wearing a night-dress. She was shivering violently. Harry stood and threw his camo jacket to the floor, took off his thick ribbed jumper and put it over the child's head, carefully threading her arms through. He lifted her up, propping her against the nearest pine and began to rub warmth into her body. He started with her arms, vigourously working down. She was tiny, her bones like needles.

"Oww!" she yelled, but he didn't stop.

She watched him and he saw her face clearly; it was round, apart from a pointed chin; her eyes were bright and wet. He started to massage her bare feet and she screamed. Harry felt her ankles; they were scratched and swollen.

Taking off his fingerless gloves he slipped them over her wounded toes, then picked up his jacket and wrapped it around her shoulders, tying the arms tight across her chest to secure it. He began to shiver in time with her, their teeth clacking in the darkness.

He searched for his thermos and, carefully pouring out tea, put the plastic cup up to the girl's lips. She felt the hot melt of steam on her face and took a sip, looking up at him.

"Who are you?" she asked. The back of her throat stuck, her voice sounded strange.

The question was sudden. Harry stuttered; "Um, Harry. L–little Harry."

"That's stupid," the girl said.

He smiled; "Yeah. I know. Got it at school, it's a nickname."

He gave her the cup and leant up against the next pine, his hands behind him, palms flat against the tree, tracing the grooves of stretch marks in its trunk. *Everything's all right, she's not hurt, she's gonna to be fine.*

"Who a'you then?" he asked.

"My name's Anne, but they call me Annie here. That's my dog, Bess." Her voice was different, Harry hadn't heard one like it before. It was very precise.

Annie took another hot gulp. Bess limped over and snuggled down next to her. She stroked the pup's muzzle, paused, then asked, "What were you doing to my dog?"

"What?"

"Bess, she woke me, she was squealing. I ran out looking for her, I ran for ages, then I saw you. What were you doing?" Harry noticed the girl's neat, white teeth glistening with spittle.

"He was caught in that snare, I got him out."

Annie leant over and checked Bess, then felt the wool scarf covering the animal's paw.

"Did you put that there?"

"Aye."

"Oh." She relaxed. "Well, anyway, *she* isn't a he."

"Oh, right."

He had never talked like this, at least not to a stranger, in the forest in the dead of night. He liked her. "Why's she wearing that?" he asked.

"What?"

"On her back end there, and that thing around her neck."

"They're trousers. That's a wig. It's fallen off."

"Why?"

"She was Elvis."

"What?"

"My dad makes me dress her up as Elvis."

"Oh." Harry reached out and patted the dog, confused. "You frum round here then?"

"I live the other side of the wood –" Her voice trailed off.

At that moment Samson came down an aisle of pines.

He walked straight to the puppy and sniffed it. Annie reached out for her dog.

"Don't worry he's mine," Harry said, "Samson's his name."

The lurcher lay down, unconcerned. Annie stared at it; it was huge and dark like the man. She let go of Bess.

Up in the trees a flock of redpolls sounded their buzzing nasal trill. Dawn was coming. Harry took the plastic cup still gripped tight in Annie's small hands, stood and packed his thermos. "Me and Samson's going to take you home, love, where a' your mam and dad then?"

"My mum's dead," Annie said.

Harry was silent.

"I live with my dad, over there." She pointed into the darkness.

It was then Harry knew the girl was a Pritchard. He remembered something about Bert Pritchard coming home with a woman from outside, then her leaving, but he didn't know about a girl.

Annie had started to cry, quietly, bubbles of spit coming from her lips. She was tired, her feet hurt. Harry moved towards her, unsure of what to do. He rifled through his knapsack, offered her a bit of pork pie, some apple. He even tried mam's fruitcake, kneeling down and stuffing a piece in her mouth, because girls like cake. She started to choke, the dark brown sponge drooling down her chin. Harry wiped her face with his shirt sleeve and she began to calm. He liked her face. It was the touch more than anything; soft and full.

She curled into a ball. Harry leant over and picked up the sleeping pup, then touched the girl, gently. She uncurled, opening her arms, and he gathered her up.

By the time he reached the stile, Annie was asleep. Her arms, swallowed by the jumper, were gripped around his neck. Bess, still in trousers, the wig hanging from her collar, was snoozing. He carried the dog in the crook of his arm, like an uncocked gun.

OKIGBO
Pimper's Paradise

Okigbo was born in the Ivory Coast in 1971. He lives in London. Pimper's Paradise is the first chapter of a novel.

Marcus Linn woke up, rubbed his bloodshot eyes and picked up the receiver.

"… ello! Hello!"

He hung up. He was sure he'd heard the phone ring. He closed his eyes for a few minutes, wondering which one of his past relationships could be responsible for the call. His watch was lying on a pile of library books on his bedside cabinet. He could hear it ticking. The noise lulled him into deeper thought.

After a while life turns into a vicious circle. Days become blurry and blend into one. It becomes difficult to tell dreams apart from reality.

Facing the ceiling he fumbled in his bedside cabinet for a pack of cigarettes. He withdrew his hand almost immediately and sighed. He'd stopped smoking years ago. His movements were out of habit. It surfaced whenever he was agitated or thinking.

He'd traced the calls a few times in the past only to recognise Aisha's new phone number.

But that was over a decade ago; it could be anyone now.

Aisha was his wife. They were still married, but he liked to refer to himself as a single man. He'd had five partners since their separation.

He and Aisha were together for four years. They got on best in bed so naturally that's where they spent most of their time. She had her friends and he had his. Sometimes on good days when she finished work early and he wasn't busking, they met at 'The Blue Anchor', a pub near Tottenham Court Road tube station. There they would talk about him, about her, then… about him again. If they were feeling optimistic, less cynical about their relationship – a mood perhaps fuelled by the endless humping on his mind, they discussed his day's busking. This usually took place on the bus, on their way to that tired old bed with loose springs.

She rarely spoke about her job. Perhaps she felt he wouldn't be interested. Perhaps he should have asked. Then again he may not have seen any point in doing so. He didn't particularly like her regimented life, her perfumes and her make-up in the morning.

Aisha had a friendly open face; always smiling. Although she was nineteen, she underestimated the affect that her behaviour and enticing figure had on the opposite sex. The thought of her flirting with the rich, fat old lecherous men desperate to grope at her youth and femininity repulsed Marcus. Sometimes his imagination took him further than he would have liked, to some hotel room where he would find her under some fat dollop of grease pounding away with a sugary grin on his face. The sight would sicken his soul.

Anyway, one day after two kids, a boy and a girl, Marcus woke up not in love anymore. The truth was he had never been in love.

Randy for four years! ... Some shit!

He drifted back to sleep and soon he was dreaming. The phone rang.

"Hello! Yes!"

His mouth begged for toothpaste, he could smell it.

"Yes... morning. I'll be there, don't worry."

It stank of morning breath, of stale saliva.

"Wednesday, I'll be there... Nine sharp... Coz I have to be at the studio at twelve... It's the last day of recording." He cleared his throat. "Yeh man! My album will soon be out on the streets." He laughed. "No doubt me! Did you call earlier? ...Probably some bitch."

Marcus believed, his last girlfriend, like most of the others, couldn't handle his lifestyle. The pounding away all night, the sleeping all day, and unexpected friends visiting at all hours, was too much for them.

He picked his nose whilst talking. His snot was dry and hard, having been exposed to a cold night. Dislodging it was almost as painful as ripping a plaster off a fresh wound. He braced himself, then scraped the roof of one of his nostrils. There was a sudden change in his breathing.

"… Nothing, just getting comfortable."

He rolled the dough-like mucus into mini balls and flicked them towards the ceiling.

"… Listen, catch you later. I'm still fuzzy… Serious headache here. Okay, yes, later."

He hung up the phone and turned over to the large heaving mound next to him. She was mummified in his once white sheets. He couldn't remember her name. He glanced at his bedside cabinet to see if his dole cheque was still there. Then, manoeuvring himself under the covers, he placed his feet onto her side and started shoving. She threw an arm onto his torso.

"You were wonderful."

Cliche he thought, but then wondered if he really had been that good in bed. He shoved her again.

"Ow, what are you doing? …Ow! You're hurting me!"

"Get out of my bed," he said calmly, "come on, get out… "

"If this is a joke I'm not laughing," she said, "I'm not into kinky games."

"And I'm not into you," he replied. "I was drunk, high – must have been."

He shoved her once more. She fell onto the floor, shrieking.

"Put on your clothes and get out."

"You're sick!" she hissed.

"Who wouldn't be at the sight of you."

She hurled insults at him whilst putting her clothes on. She was trembling, her piercing voice cut through his head like knife stabs. A night of substance abuse had left him brittle. He felt like throwing up, but instead he watched her with little expression on his face. He was surprised by how ugly she was. She had dark, yellow rims round her eyes, brown wiry hair which looked as if it had never been combed. He could still smell her armpits on his covers. She was well-proportioned; her breasts were firm, but they curved inwards at the bottom, so that her nipples faced each other. Once she was dressed to his satisfaction, he got out of bed. He was naked. He grabbed her handbag, her hair, and dragged her out of his front door. By now she was hysterical:

"I'll call the police! I'll call the… "

"Go ahead!" he said. "You'll be the one arrested. Don't you

know it's an offence for ugly bitches like you to take advantage of drunk men?"

He slammed the door in her face.

"Who wants to stay in that shithole anyway?" she yelled. "… Fucking busker! Tramp! Coke-Head! … Nigger!"

Her last word froze him.

"Who wants to stay in that shithole?" He bellowed, "… well, you ask your arse, coz my dick's already told me where I was staying last night! … Bitch!"

Surprised by his own loudness, he fell silent.

"Bastard!" She yelled. "… Bastard!"

He walked off towards the bathroom as though she was no longer on his mind.

There was only one person who figured much in his thoughts these days. She was an African woman who graced the dingy underground tunnels that made up his office.

Her presence in his mind softened his heart and changed his mood. He didn't know her name or which part of the continent she came from, but he liked to think of her as an Ethiopian queen. He'd heard of their beauty and elegance. She was very tall and had an infectious smile which seemed to radiate warmth right through to his bones.

He hated the working masses, but his Ethiopian queen was an exception. She was the only person that could make him whole again after a hard day spent underground breathing station soot.

Marcus would sit with his guitar at the far corner of the tunnel to the Central or Northern line, singing and playing; watching people approach. He would listen to the coins dropping onto the leather case next to him. He would always try to acknowledge those who left him something. Some walked past, genuinely buried in thought. Not all though, after a while he got to know the pretenders. Those who distracted themselves just before they got to him. Others felt ashamed of seeing a fellow black man stoop so low in society. The sad thing was, some of these men in slick suits, carrying mobile phones, recognised him. Marcus had seen them many a time in his neighbourhood, on street corners, in dark alleys. He'd seen them exchanging parcels, selling one illegal item or another. He'd seen teenagers, peering through half-open back windows of houses.

He'd seen their white counterparts too, doing the same things in their own way, their own style. He resented their judgmental eyes. Often he felt like rushing at them, bashing their heads against the walls of the underground, bashing out their cynical motives, as if that would seal his position as the better person. But that rage was always controlled.

Marcus had no illusions about his place in society. He knew exactly where he was and how far down people had to look to find him strumming away at his guitar. But there was nothing like the odd smile from a passer-by, an acknowledgement, or the occasional request. Although they never left him feeling as good as his Ethiopian queen could, they lifted his spirit out of the long spells of indignation he had to endure every day.

He knew he was no star: something a lot of his fellow buskers tended to forget. Half of those who paid him compliments were just passing through his world, on their way to better lives. His music, so long as he was performing in the tube station, would never be enticing enough to keep his audience from catching the first train. For them, he was merely a bridge between the depressing tones of the underground and the collection of CDs of favourite bands and solo artists at home. He was a jukebox with no set price to switch him on.

He headed straight for the window in his lounge, peering through his curtains to see if his one-night-stand was still there. He felt guilty about the way he had treated her, but he was also angry. Angry and ashamed with himself for having slept with a stranger. Somehow she had come between him and his feelings for his Ethiopian queen.

A widow and full-time busybody, who lived in a block of council flats opposite his, mirrored his movements. She looked down through her dark curtains onto the pavement then up at his window. He went into the kitchen; made some toast, switched on the TV and collapsed back onto the bed. He flicked through the channels, preoccupied with his thoughts.

Feeling rich after an unusually good day's busking, and positive about his music project, he'd spent last night on cocaine and alcohol. This morning, he was in no mood to busk. He thought of making a cup of coffee, but felt too weak.

Four men in a newly formed band strutted their stuff in front of him on the TV. The familiar trendy hairstyles, pretty looks and synthetic sound, packaged as one image, taunted him with that fame he was hoping to capture with his debut album.

"Time will tell," he muttered to himself.

His life had to be tougher than theirs: he didn't have the looks, and reggae wasn't exactly high on the agendas of any of the major record labels. He'd been in the music business for almost twenty years, just about surviving, practically in debt all the time. He would have to do most of the promotion work himself. Relying on his talent, hard work and persistence. But he didn't mind, music allowed the sun to shine through to his soul, it gave him a reason to open his eyes every morning.

The phone rang again. Marcus hesitated, allowing it to ring a few more times. It stopped at the fourth. He sighed. A few minutes passed. He looked at his watch; it was 10.30 a.m. He dragged himself off his bed, brushed his teeth before having a quick wash. The water was cold. He'd forgotten to switch on the immersion heater. He breathed deeply, trying to suppress the shock it had on his system.

After a few minutes he stepped out of the shower and dried himself slowly whilst looking into the mirror. He looked at his physique, breathed in now and then, puffed out his chest and turned sideways to look at his profile from a different angle. He looked at himself with questioning interest, like a cosmetic surgeon, assessing himself, trying to decide which parts of his body would have to be trimmed to enhance his looks.

His clothes were strewn all over the floor from the bathroom to his bed. He'd peeled them off in his drunken stupor before crashing naked onto his bed.

Or... on top of the stranger he'd just kicked out?

He couldn't recall anything about her. Whether he'd asked her back or she'd invited herself he didn't have a clue. His boxer shorts were still in his track suit bottoms. He picked them up, threw them to one side and searched for a clean pair. He sniffed each item of clothing before putting it on.

Once dressed, he stared at the mirror one last time, shook his dreadlocks and shouted:

"Confrontation!"

It was his cry for another battle, for another day of struggling against any indignation he endured as a busker.

He grabbed his leather jacket and guitar, and stepped outside into a cold but gentle breeze. The sun was shining through candy-floss clouds. Spring was in full strut.

"Wednesday," he said to himself.

He still had a long wait before his album would be out on the streets, but at least the recording was nearly over. Soon he would be taking a fresh step into a different stage of his life. A faint smile meddled with the street-wise look on his face. An expression he adopted whenever he was in his neighbourhood or in similar poor areas. He nodded at a few familiar faces queuing to get on the same bus as him.

He thought of his Ethiopian queen. She reminded him of a song, which he had not heard in a long time: … *You're… the Lily of my valley…* the words came to him, then lingered in the back of his thoughts.

He wondered whether he would see her today. The rarity of her smile seemed more precious to him than anything he could gain from a day's busking. She never gave him any money, but somehow she fed him with her presence when he was hungry. He drank the trail of sweet enchantment she left behind in the tunnels. He feasted on her every movement, her shapely backside, which moved with elegance to a perfect, subtle rhythm in his mind. He relished her tall, slim, well-proportioned figure, as it disappeared amongst the rush of people.

She loved reggae music and would often stop to chat with him when he was playing. Her voice was deep, yet soft and whispery. It was, for him, a fresh breeze in the underground. Sometimes she would just say: "Hi… " then listen to him playing for a while. Passengers would stop to watch them both.

Inspired by her presence, he would make half his day's earnings during these short periods.

The bus arrived. Marcus boarded it and sat down. He thought about the last time he'd seen his Ethiopian queen. It had been almost a fortnight, when he was sitting at the end of the tunnel to the central line during rush hour, playing around with his guitar, trying to remember the words of a song.

"Hello, Marcus."

Marcus looked up, surprised and yet sure of whom he would find staring down at him. She was smiling.

"Oh... hi!" he said, trying not to sound excited, "... long time."

"Yes... how's your family?"

"Fine!" he replied without thinking.

He hadn't seen his children or any of his relatives in months. He often wondered why she asked about them. He knew that she was being polite.

But why did she presume he had a family? He wasn't wearing a wedding ring...

"Eez that a new song you're writing? It sounds nice."

"Oh no, I wish... " Marcus replied. "It's 'Pick Myself Up', by Peter Tosh."

"Aah, don"t be so humble. Your songs are as good you know?"

Marcus smiled and glanced at a black man standing close to her. The man was staring at him with slight repugnance. He was in his mid-thirties. He wore a green suit. His top shirt buttons were undone, exposing a thin gold chain. His tie hung loosely round his neck. He forced a smile onto his face and nodded at Marcus. Marcus was about to respond, but then he noticed that the man was fumbling for something in his trouser pockets and looked away. The man chucked a few coins onto his guitar casing. Marcus pretended not to hear the noise the money made.

"You're too nice to me you know... "

For a moment they were both smiling, but then she remembered that they weren't alone:

"Peter... "

The man in the suit stepped forward, ready to be introduced.

"This guy is going to be famous one day, you know."

He glanced at Marcus and smiled.

"I know, I can see that." His voice carried little emotion.

"Mark my words," she said. "he will."

Marcus chuckled as though embarrassed, all the time aware of, and taking pleasure in, the man's increasing irritation.

"Anyway," Marcus said, changing the subject, "how's your day been?"

"Very, very, busy... too busy." She looked at the man next to her. "Peter is a work colleague."

Marcus glanced at him and nodded.

She yawned, "Gosh, I am so tired."

He looked at the man again, this time smiling...

A morose voice distanced him from his thoughts:

"Tickets please!"

He fumbled for his wallet. Then chuckled at the way his Ethiopian queen had risen above the petty emotions of the man who'd looked down on him. She never felt ashamed to stop and talk to him – that was partly what he found so enchanting about her.

Sometimes they talked about visiting reggae artists performing in town. She was always keen to know where they were playing, but Marcus often wondered whether she ever went to see them. She never spoke about these concerts again and the impact of her beauty, the short duration of their conversation, always pushed such questions out of his thoughts.

Perhaps it slipped her mind too? Perhaps she had no one to go with?

Marcus could not imagine the man he'd seen her with in casual clothes, let alone at a roots reggae concert. He doubted whether she knew anyone who would be willing to abandon their pretentious life for a night at the Brixton Academy, listening to the relentless pounding of poverty, anti-establishment songs, immersed in ganja filled air.

He jumped off the bus just before it reached Tottenham Court Road Underground. A combination of knowing that his album would soon be complete, the sun, and the boisterous mood of

Oxford Street left him in a positive frame of mind. He slung his guitar onto his back like a rifle. There was a spring to his every step. He was a man on a mission.

What his Ethiopian queen needed was a laid-back brother like him, some excitement in her life ... a spliff or two, maybe.

He wondered if she ever smoked. She didn't look the type. He started to undress her in his mind. Someone bumped the thought out of his head and promptly apologised.

"Yo Marcus, long time, where have you been?"

It was David; he worked on the underground.

"Where have *you* been?"

David laughed. He had a deep tan. He was Scottish but had a pseudo American accent, probably acquired from listening to too much rap music; or watching Hollywood movies.

"I guess the tan says it all!" Marcus said. "... The good life hey?"

"Yeah well, tried to get myself one of those exotic tans. You know, like yours? ... What's the secret maan? Where do you go on holiday?"

"Right here in London," replied Marcus.

"Well that's some mean sun-bed!"

They both laughed and looked around to see if any other station staff were near. David let Marcus through the barriers.

"Where have you been anyway?"

"Trinidad! ... Sunshine! Women and coconuts! ... Not to mention a lickle weed," he murmured with a cheeky grin on his face.

"That's nice. Here I am, can't even afford to go back to my roots. You go there, on holiday, without telling me. Come back, and then take the piss out of *my* poverty and *me*."

"I didn't know... "

"Did you ask? Did you tell me you were going on holiday?"

David smiled, he knew that Marcus was joking but he still felt uncomfortable.

Someone appeared from a 'Staff Only' door and looked at them suspiciously. Marcus, with his eyes, alerted him of the man's presence and headed down the escalator.

The station was unusually quiet. The pitch was empty. It was near a clock, at the far end of the southbound, Northern line platform. His mates must have been recovering from the previous night of celebrating with him; none of them were around. He sat down on the floor with his back against the wall, crossed his legs and unzipped his guitar-case. He sighed and pulled out his instrument. He stared blankly at the clock for a moment – as its second hand jerked round: tick... tick... tick... till it reached another number on its dusty face. Somehow its characters lost their meaning under the permanent glare of the station lights. No one seemed to pay the clock much attention anymore. The new digital installations were much easier to read.

He played a lot of his own songs, and the occasional rock classic, to ensure that coins kept dropping into his guitar case. Twice he stopped and chatted with familiar faces. He busked for just under two hours before taking a break.

Outside the air had warmed up a little. He expected to see his friends at the local cafe but they weren't there either. He ordered some chips and a cup of black coffee and sat at a table by the entrance. There seemed to be a lot of tourists in the place. He gulped down his food, seldom looking up. He listened to a couple, not too far off:

"So where are you from?" The voice sounded Scandinavian.

"Iyam from the U.S.A." The man spoke with an African accent.

"Which part? You don't sound American... "

"Yeh man, I used to be in the marines... stationed in West Africa."

"Wow, what was Africa like?"

"It was great! I made a lot of friends out there... and the wild life... Woo! It was beautiful! Magnifique!" He kissed the tip of his fingers. "... Lions! Tigers! ... So much of it!"

"I have always wanted to go to Africa, Kenya, maybe now South Africa."

"Maybe I can take you there one day?"

She said nothing, but Marcus sensed she was smiling.

"You're very beautiful," he continued.

Marcus looked up towards them. The man's enormous hands covered a blond woman's on the table. His clothes looked as if they were once expensive. He wore a seventies linen suit, which was white. His trousers had been narrowed at the bottom for the eighties. He did not look comfortable in them. He was a huge black man with heavy features. His half-afro, turned flat-top at a last minute's thought, beefed up his big head. He grinned non-stop. He had a booming voice that seemed to come from everywhere.

"Have you ever been with a black man before?"

She hesitated.

"No."

He smiled, looking down into her eyes. There was sweat on his forehead. Their faces were almost touching.

"I could tear you apart... You'll love it!"

Marcus shuddered, wondering how the man's charm had managed to upstage his outfit. He felt like saying something, but remembered his one-night-stand.

The blond woman moved her left hand until it was lost under the table. The man tightened his grip on her right arm. She pulled away, shuffled her chair backwards, then bent forward and ducked under the tablecloth. Marcus held his breath. The man was still grinning; his teeth gleamed through the darkness of his sweaty skin. All of a sudden she got up with a bag in her hand.

"Let's go!" she said.

The man stuffed a last handful of chips on his plate into his mouth, quickly washed it down with a glass of beer and followed her. She paid the bill.

Laughter broke out behind Marcus as the couple hurried out, chasing their lust to some obscure bed, somewhere in the city. Marcus chuckled, sipping at his lukewarm coffee. The talk and laughter behind him continued.

He stared out of the cafe window, registering little. One of the voices behind him began to grow familiar. It giggled a lot, occasionally breaking into half shrieks. Marcus listened for a while, determined to identify it without turning around.

A waiter cleared his table impatiently, but he held on to his practically empty cup of coffee. Two men stood by the doorway, waiting to be seated. Now and then they glanced in his direction.

The woman who giggled a lot hardly said a word. There was a certain resonance in her voice, which softened her tone; it made her sound black. The man with her was well spoken. Marcus couldn't work out what he was saying, but she seemed to be enjoying his company. Finally he put down his cup, counted the correct amount of money for the meal and headed for the counter.

He kept looking around for the couple as he walked. He paid with mostly ten and twenty-pence coins. Eventually he located the two voices. They were sitting at the rear end of the cafe, away from other customers. The woman had her back to Marcus. She was very dark and slim. He could now detect her African accent. The man was good looking, well groomed. His close-cut goatee and the thin smear of a moustache were an attempt to look refined. He was wearing a black leather jacket. He had one gold front tooth. He didn't notice Marcus watching them. His deep voice resonated from their corner. The rise and fall of the woman's giggles punctuated it. Cigarette smoke escaped from his mouth, curling into the air above him.

Marcus watched them, thinking of his Ethiopian queen. No one paid him any attention. Time had stopped; his world was silent. After what must have only been a few seconds, he shook his head briskly, then muttered:

"Maybe in the next life."

There was sadness in his eyes. He sighed and glanced around him. Then smiled in an attempt to lift his spirit.

He flung his guitar onto his back and stepped out of the cafe, heading for the bus stop. It was 3.30 p.m. Rush hour wasn't too far off, but he had lost the will to busk for the day.

A sudden weariness gripped him as his bus drifted down Tottenham Court Road. Bob Marley wafted up out of a car window, seeping into his melancholy. Marcus listened to his words:

"A pimper's paradise, that's all she was. A pimper's paradise, that's all she was… "

Slowly his eyes closed. The rest of the song found its way into his subconscious. It played over and over again until he was asleep.

He woke up in bed alone, sniffed. A bit of coke left in his nostrils knocked him back into yesterday for a few seconds. The room was cold. His curtains were wide open. Outside, somewhere above his flat, a promising day was already loosing its brilliance to a stretch of grey clouds. It was Monday morning. Time to busk again.

JOHNNY RICH

from *A Human Script*

Johnny Rich lives in South London, having failed to move more than a mile from where he was born in 1969. In an effort to avoid working for a living, he has spent the last ten years writing and editing a series of guidebooks and freelancing in journalism, television and public relations. This extract is from his first novel.

J*esus*, I say, although maybe not out loud as the taxi pulls up outside Dunmarrick Free Presbyterian Kirk. It is not a prayer.

I've just had to catch a cab all the way from the Kirkcaldy Station and it's costing me twenty quid and I'm paying in English notes and I'm still late for my own father's funeral anyway. It's raining – it should always rain at funerals – but it's only an April shower. I grab my red nylon overnight bag, tighten my borrowed tie and sneak in at the back, trying not to make a sound with the bloody ridiculously noisy doors that all churches insist on having.

I do not want to be here.

But it's not a matter of choice. Being late is bad enough.

The terminal condition of the late Eugene Joseph Putnam had skulked in the shadows for some time. Since his birth, in fact, but it had been particularly notable during the last four months. His imminent death was first heralded by headaches in the shower and a craving for honey, followed by a stroke just after Christmas. His decline had been fast once the prognosis was decreed, his body ceding to the edict that he should die. Since his beginning, his end was only a matter of time and the duration of the inevitable mechanism was sixty-five years.

Eugene was tall and thin with granite grey hair across the chin, above the ears and sparsely across the head under his Homburg hat. He had been known as Gene to his friends. Among these, he would have numbered the members of the independent Calvinist congregation of the kirk, a cautious selection of other inhabitants of Dunmarrick and its neighbouring villages (mainly the managers of small local businesses) and, of course, William Laing, to whom he referred as "my partner in crime". Such terminology passed as humour among the employees and clients of Putnam & Laing (Solicitors) Ltd., although, in fact, wills, conveyancing and the occasional commercial contract were more common than criminal casework in rural Fife.

Many of these friends are attending the funeral, presided over by the Reverend Clifford Macallan BA, as well as a number of relatives.

He was also called 'Gene' by his son Dan. On growing out of 'Daddy', Dan had insisted on 'Gene' despite – indeed, because of – the thin-lipped sneer it would provoke amid the stony beard. Chris, on the other hand, tried to call him 'Dad' and then 'Father'. And then he stopped calling him. But Gene stopped calling Chris anything first, anything but names, names which were both intended, and taken, as insults.

They spoke to each other for the last time more than five years before Gene died. Chris was unable to remember what those last words had been, but he knew (though would never acknowledge) they were said more in sorrow than in anger.

I am not so late it seems. I sit in a pew near the back. Bare white plastered walls and high leaden windows. Dan glances at me from the aisle where he moves among the people and he throws me a smile. He'll be alright through this. He's the star of the show, number one mourner, and, if there's anything he's good at, it's playing to the crowd. I look back at him and hope he'll know that the only thing I want right now is not to be like him, not to be the centre. Keep that look between us, just us. Don't get me down the front, Dan. Don't get me to sit with the family. Don't even let on that I'm here. Let me be a ghost. Let me be.

Dan is guiding Great Aunt Polly to a seat. He keeps saying loudly that she can sit at the front with the rest of the family so she can hear, but it's no good because she can't even hear Dan. So she's trying to sit down on every row as they move slowly down the aisle and the people already sitting in the rows move up to make space for her, but they're uncertain because everyone else in the kirk has heard Dan, except Aunt Polly. So each time she makes as if to sit down, Dan takes her arm again and leads her further to the front, saying, "You'll hear better at the front... I said, you'll hear better at the front."

When we buried Mummy, it was terrible. My father sat in the kitchen and ate breakfast, dipping dry toast in his egg with his wife about to go in the ground. Stinging eyes I had and the silence was so wide I thought I'd hear nothing again until I heard the sound of my father, my father crying. Little weeps, the only time. And I didn't believe him.

But this, this is just comic. I think I feel nothing. Except I want to giggle, to break the awful quiet if nothing else. To give these cold stiffs in their dark coats a jolt, to let them know that, yes, actually, the *other* son has turned up. But I wouldn't. Dan might, if he were me, but me, no.

Dan's voice does break the quiet to say, "Here. Just here. And here's the order of service." Great Aunt Polly takes the folded, stapled sheets from him. There is sound, I realise. There has been all along, I just didn't hear it before. The sound of the organ playing dully and low, echoing in the cold grey nave. It doesn't sound like music, just random sighs of sound. Also, there are people talking. I did not notice it before or maybe they weren't talking then. I watch lips chatter incessantly and steamy wisps of breath, but all I hear is murmur, and I watch them nod solemnly. None of these sounds is distinct from silence.

Probably not even thirty-five. What's that? Barely one for every two years of his life. And look at them, like walking dead themselves. Reverend Macallan is in the pulpit now, from somewhere. The congregation rises and bows. I rise too.

I realise my father is there. Or, at least, his coffin is. I had not noticed it before. It had seemed an extension of the altar, some kind of furniture, but he is in there. Or, at least, his body is there. That box surely cannot be large enough to fit the corpse that was my father. I could just run up there and shove it and then he'd spill out and I picture him staring at me in horror from his box.

There can't be a body in there. No-one would know if they filled it with weights. He can't be in there.

But his body is, within that thin wall of wood. What else survives now? Dust to dust. Systems shut down, till only the hair and fingernails carry farcically on. It's all reflex, just like twitching frog's legs in dissections. Is there air in there that might make the hair twitch? His grey hair will still be growing, but slow, no twitching.

How bizarre, how pagan it all is, bringing a cadaver into a place of worship.

"I am the resurrection and the life: he that believeth in me, though he were dead, yet shall he live. And whosoever liveth and believeth in me shall never die. Let us sing together psalm 16." The organ starts off-key, I think, and a few bold-hearted stalwarts know when to join in.

"Where are we?" says Great Aunt Polly loudly enough to be heard over the dirge to my uncle Morris who is sitting next to her.

"We're in the kirk, Auntie," he whispers as loudly as possible so she might hear him and the rest of the congregation might be able to pretend they haven't.

"No. In the thing." She waves her order of service and he takes it from her, turns it the right way up and hands it back to her pointing.

It is her nephew in that box. And Morris's big brother. Or his body at least. My daddy is not any more. If I lifted the lid – if they do not nail it down – my father's hands would be cold and grey, but my daddy is a warm, dry hand holding mine on a walk on a cold fresh day when the air tastes like peppermint and I kick through leaves in red wellingtons. People don't own wellingtons in London and piles of leaves always contain dog shit.

An old man is singing too loudly. As if it helps.

So my father wins, in the end, and he knew he would. He always knew that one way or another he would get me back into this kirk. I imagine him saying, "Son, my son, thou wilt return to a knowledge of Christ, for it is foreknown. Taint not thy mind. I will make thee return, if it's the last thing I ever do." But he never said anything like that.

We said family prayers and I used to like it, giggling with Dan at the big table in the dark kitchen every morning and as we spoke, often it was cold enough for the words to form brief clouds. I used to think they were like the breath of dragons. But family prayers are for families. I don't remember what we did when mummy went and that was not so long before I came away. Six years, more than six years, my father lived in that house all alone. Dan didn't believe the prayers any more than I did, but he could forget them the moment we said "amen". Even now, look at him, with his earnest look, listening to the Reverend Macallan who stands swaddled in his black geneva gown and reading in a dark monotone like an older man.

He's the other son, not me. Why am *I* sitting at the back at my father's funeral? Why do all these people think it is *me* who is so unspeakable? In London, it is Dan. Dan is the outrageous one. Dan is the one who sleeps around, who takes drugs and doesn't have a proper job. And I, I am not a black sheep anywhere, anywhere but here.

"But by the grace of God I am what I am," reads Reverend Macallan, "and his grace which was bestowed upon me was not in vain; but I laboured more abundantly than they all: yet not I, but the grace of God which was with me."

I am what I am. I think of Gloria Gaynor, is it? But she sings it as if it's a statement of choice, of freedom. *I am what I am and what I am needs no excuses.* These people, nodding their grey heads, accept it as their destinies, saved or not, by God's irresistible grace. And they all think they're saved.

"The last enemy that shall be destroyed is death."

Junk. Ninety-five percent of this is junk. Dad dies. Mummy died. I will die. And that's how people, animals, plants go on living. Regeneration through recombination and selection. There is no resurrection. There is no god. Daddy isn't in that box. I know what death is, it's the price we pay for sex – it's what they taught me week one, biology degree.

"If after the manner of men I have fought with beasts at Ephesus, what advantageth it me, if the dead rise not? Let us eat and drink; for tomorrow we die." Reverend Macallan looks up from the lectern. He speaks again in a softer tone, "Please rise and let us read together." And everyone stands up and everyone except me and Great Aunt Polly seems to shuffle their order of service and they start chanting together. There are tulips on the altar. It is late April.

A small boy, five, maybe, is standing on a pew a few rows in front of me next to a woman who is probably his mother – but I don't know these people. He gets down from the seat and his head disappears.

"Please sit," says Reverend Macallan. Up, down. Is all this necessary to commune with God? He pauses, looks around as people sit. He does not see a small boy's head bob up in the pew in front of me. The boy stares at me and smiles and I can't help but smile back and then he ducks down. "We are gathered here to mourn the passing of Eugene Putnam, to give thanks for his life and to celebrate that he is now received into our Father's house. He was a dear friend and neighbour to us all and this congregation, this parish, will especially feel his loss."

He goes on – chairman of the parish council, treasurer of the parish council, chairman again. Solicitor. Freemason. Regular contributor of letters to the editor in *The Scotsman* and other newspapers. Free thinker and follower of John Calvin in all his teachings.

"But most of all," says Reverend Macallan as if he knew anything about my father, "he was a loving family man. By the grace of God, he joins his wife Mary who went before him into the kingdom of heaven six years ago, his father Eugene David and his mother Wendy.

"He leaves his three brothers and his two sons, Daniel" – he glances at the front row – "and Christopher." Who, I would point out, is also here, is also in a church, also doing his mourning, also... I don't know. But I don't say anything. I cannot. I am what I am, but I am not one who speaks out in crowds. Hasn't he noticed me? I am invisible. I hope I am invisible. I want to be here, witness it, but perhaps to run around yanking black ties, knocking off the women's hats, strewing tulips in the air. My own celebration of his life. My own fury that he left without a word.

The old man who was singing too loudly is blowing his nose. This place smells of mildew, of creeping black cultures redoubling on prayer books.

"We are all born in sin. It lives in every part of us, but God, in His goodness, has chosen some of us to be saved although none of us are worthy of His love." The little boy pops his head up again in front of me and smiles. I smile back briefly and look again towards the pulpit, trying to be appropriate, but the boy continues to stare at me smiling.

"He has given us His only son in atonement for the sins of the elect, as Jesus said in his suffering, 'I pray not for the world, but for them which thou hast given me; for they are thine.' And we are saved not by our own will, but by God's and we shall know those whom He has chosen by their acts and by their sincere knowledge of Christ. Gene Putnam was such a man." The boy laughs, still staring at me. No-one turns around. He bobs down again.

"Rarely was there a man so clearly destined by God to join Him in His glory. God has saved him. Gene was free to act according to the good nature with which God blessed him and the goodness of his nature meant he was never free to stray from the path of righteousness."

He honestly believes it all. What sort of freedom is that? Freedom to do what God has made you choose to do? Why does he go on believing it? There is no God and I have no father. Take the body away. Do what you want with it. And try resurrecting the bones.

The boy runs down the aisle from the back of the kirk. "Wooo, wooe, wooee," he screams and it makes a fine echo between the grey walls. Everyone looks. No-one speaks. A hand darts out from an aisle and grabs him and his elasticated trouser band slips slightly and he falls over and starts to cry.

"We who loved him may share our grief together, express our thanks for his life and rejoice that he now resides with Christ."

The little boy cries. People glare at his mother. My father is saved. I am not. I have no knowledge of Christ. The rest might as well be silence.

In every living thing, there are cells. Sometimes one, sometimes so many they are beyond reckoning. And in every cell, there is a nucleus. And in every nucleus, there is DNA[1].

---

[1] With the exception of certain simple life forms which have only ribose

In every cell[2] in every body of every member of
that arbitrarily determined group called 'human', there
are two metres of DNA. Stretched out, it would be
taller than most specimens of the species, but it is not.
It is wound beyond the gaze of microscopes in plaited
spirals, which disentangle, duplicate and recombine as
each cell divides. Copies upon copies, clone upon
clone of identical DNA, copied in their trillions throughout
the human frame from brain to bone and from muscle to the
very marrow.

In every cell in every body in every living thing,
DNA is written in a language of only four letters. A, C, G, T.
Each letter represents a chemical. Adenine, Cytosine,
Guanine, Thymine. In the language of DNA, there are just
three letters in every word and each word means one
amino acid. There are only sixty-four words, but even so, many
are synonyms: there are only twenty meanings, only twenty
amino acids.

Everything is an anagram and words are never meaningless.

In every cell in every body in every living thing, strings of
words make sentences: meanings locked together to make a
protein. A sentence is a single gene. In every human cell, there
are perhaps one hundred thousand genes. The sentences make
up chapters: in every human cell, there are forty-six
chromosomes, twenty-three pairs. The chapters make a book:
the human genome contains more than three billion letters.
Three thousand million. Three thousand thousand thousand.
Thirty hundred hundred hundred hundred. Twice.

If humankind has an essence, here it is writ.

The Human Genome Project will inscribe the human
manuscript. The three billion letters will be written down for all
time. Even some of the known variations will be noted, those

---

nucleic acid (RNA) rather than deoxyribose nucleic acid (DNA) and
simpler forms yet which might not even be termed 'life'. Prions, for
example, or inteins.
[2] With the exception of the 'gametes' or sex-cells: the spermatozoa in
the male; the ova in the female.

typographical changes that make every folio unique, that perpetually corrupt the pure text of humanity as some author might have once intended it to be. For Adam and Eve have been degraded, reduplicated forever, photocopies of photocopies, never the exact same mistakes. If God wrote the human script in his own image, then it is by now, a travesty. If the Script wrote itself, there was never any first folio nor ever shall there be a last. Now Man is writing it out, and it will be long.

The Human Genome Project is the most expensive scientific project ever. To travel two metres of DNA is costing more than a journey of one quarter of a million miles of space to set a human foot upon the moon.

The Human Genome Project offers a new Rosetta stone. It is the hope of decyphering those sicknesses carved on the ovum's membrane by the etching of a sperm. It is the chance to crack the icon of cancer and vanquish for evermore that ball of death inside. It will even smash the tablets on which mortality itself is inscribed. In the laboratories of the world labour the millennial explorers. For they are the distillers of The Essence of Man. They are The Seekers of The Holy Grail. They Are The Ones Who Hold The Secret Of Life Itself.

They are the copyists.

The Human Genome is three billion letters long: A, C, G, T.

The book is nothing without meaning, without a reader to understand. The human genome is a script, waiting for the amino actors, the protein players to strut and fret their hour upon the stage in an intricate, interacting interplay. Who can say they saw a whole play or read a whole book?

Humankind cannot read the book of life. Who knows what levels of meaning are embedded in the gematria and temurah of the genome? Some genes are read forwards, some backwards. Some mean something different when repeated. Some only yield understanding when read in context. Some only yield understanding when words are ignored. Some appear to have no meaning at all. Ninety-five percent, humans used to say, is junk, meaningless. But they know now that they simply do not know how to read it.

Beyond the writing of the human script is a greater task: understanding the letters on the page.

What a piece of work is a man? The human genome!

I follow my uncles and my brother as they carry my father's coffin to the graveside, not because I want to be there as they cover the box with dirt, but because I do not want to stand and wait by the kirk with the people who do not know what to say, especially to me.

We, the close family, stand in black above this rectangular ditch to watch this rite performed, the body in the box, the box in the hole, the dirt on the box. I know what happens. I stand with my back to my mother's grave.

"I would not have you to be ignorant, brethren, concerning them which are asleep, that ye sorrow not, even as others which have no hope. For if we believe that Jesus died and rose again, even so them also which sleep in Jesus will God bring with him."

It has stopped raining, but I wish it hadn't. I don't want people to see that I am not crying. They will think terrible things of me. They already do. The sun has come out.

I am angry. I am glad. I am tired.

When I watched them throw mud on my mother's box and knew it was just a box, I think that was the nail in the coffin as far as God was concerned. Having no reason to believe takes you only so far, even having something else to replace it. God had his nails in me so deep, I needed a damn good reason to resent the very notion of him. If it's not too grand a thing to think, God died for me the day we buried my mother.

It is too grand. I decayed gradually.

"Wherefore comfort one another with these words."

No. I will comfort myself with thoughts of piggy-back rides and my father whom I kissed I don't know how often. And that I won't again.

The Human Genome Laboratory at Queen's College, London, where Chris works, was, in the mid 1980s, one of the first frontiers of the Human Genome Project. The first scribes of the genome cloned and recorded the DNA bases: sequencing.

This process, however, became increasingly the preserve of factory labs, vast white warehouses spinning threads of letters all night and day, never ceasing their duplication even while human bodies sleep.

In order to maintain his laboratory's snout in the trough, Sir Hugo Huttenton, the Director, specialised Queen's College's activities, focusing on the sequencing of genes related to specific pathologies and identifying where they appeared on which chromosome. The glorious tradition of the Queen's Eugenics Laboratory (as it had previously been known), the role it had played in establishing the Human Genome Project and the almost unique scientific reputation of Sir Hugo himself afforded him the opportunity to pursue funding for research which would inevitably attract public attention. Being familiar with self-generating systems, Sir Hugo reasoned that such attention would beget fame, fame would beget reputation, reputation would beget funding for research which would inevitably attract public attention. And so it was.

As a consequence, Sir Hugo and his staff concentrated increasingly on conditions which are related to single gene mutations – maybe only a single word misspelt, or a single letter out of place – and, in particular, they explore the X chromosome. The X chromosome is the most easily probed not least because, unlike chromosomes 1 to 22 which every human has in matching pairs, males have just a single X and a single Y. Females receive an X from each parent, but the X of men is always bequeathed by their mother. Their Y is handed down from their father and from his father before that unto the thousandth generation and beyond.

Until, that is, the clerks of cell division make enough mistakes to render the script unrecognisable. That, then, is a new species. Some mistakes assist meaning: if meaning means survival, the mistakes survive. Some mistakes attach themselves to those which survive. Some mistakes are part of the wastage of life. No individual survives life, but their ancestors inherit their successes and mistakes.

Outside the house, the last guests gone, Dan mentions casually as he rolls a cigarette, mid-conversation, after telling me he'd slept with the nurse, "You know, Gene did want to see you at the end."

"What?"

"Oh yeah, the whole death-bed trip."

"What?"

"The email."

"What?"

"Wotwotwot. The email. I sent it the Friday before he choked."

I remember the email. It is still unread. "I didn't get it," I say. "I was in Cambridge until the Monday and then, then I didn't, then you phoned and he was dead." Dan is already licking at the Rizla and pinching it into shape between finger and thumb. "What," I begin, "what did it say?"

"Not much. Just sort of last legs stuff and that he wanted to see you. I thought you'd ignored it." He lights the roll-up, cupping it from the wind with both hands. "Was a bit surprised at the time."

How could you? I want to scream at Dan, at his indifference, but I don't, because Dan wants to get a rise. And anyway, I did. I did ignore it. Daddy wanted to see me before he died. I didn't even want to know what it said. I wouldn't have wanted to see him anyway. I would have said no to this dying man. Would I? I don't know, no one could know, a pointless *what if?* Would I have wanted his death-bed absolution, words of frail forgiveness poured in my ear as I bent over his unrecognisable dying frame shrouded in hospital sheets? Would he have forgiven me anyhow? There was nothing to forgive. I don't want it anyway.

He should have accepted in the first place. If there's any forgiving to be done, it's by me, and would I have wanted to rush to his bedside to grant it? Out of love? Out of pity? Out of guilt?

"Why?" I ask. "Did he want to see me just to tell me I was forgiven for being me?"

"No, it was more a love thing, I think." He pauses just inside the door to see the effect on me, standing still outside. "He wanted to say that he understood. You have to be who you are. He hoped you might change in the end, but… well, he wanted to say he didn't blame you for not being one of the saved, but that it's never too late to show you are. That stuff. I think the point was that his main objection to you all along was religious and not, well, personal, and that, religiously speaking, he wanted you back. Oh yeah, and he was going to say he loved you."

These don't sound like my father's words and I am not sure whether to believe them. He knows how close I am to breaking now and maybe, maybe the words sound different because at the end, after all, there was a change. They don't sound like Dan's either, he isn't making them up. At least, not deliberately. I don't know what to think. I don't know now whether I have sinned against my father or he has sinned against me. I did not go to see him on his deathbed. But he is no longer. He's just decay in a box in the ground. It doesn't matter. But it does. He was and is no more than a tide of chemical currents, now oozing into the bottom of a coffin. But he was more.

And I didn't see him at the last. Even when he wanted me to. Dan holds my gaze and touches my arm and says something but I am not hearing it. He loved me. He fathered me. We loved my mother and he loved me so much he could not bear it for me to see him cry when she died. And I left him alone, to fumble about this house, moving the furniture around to try to make her absence go away. How can an absence go? I left him to get old and ill and be in pain and die and I would not even come when at last he wanted only for me to be there. I did not even want to know.

Dan steps aside and into the kitchen. I am still standing outside by the front door and the wind is wrapping around the house and whipping around me, sharpening itself against my cheeks and making my eyes water. I step inside and I can see through into the living room and beyond on to the patio where my father's ghost stands by the window. He beckons.

SARAH RIGBY

from *Your World*

Sarah Rigby was born in 1972 and grew up in Manchester. She is currently working on her novel, *Your World*, which is made up of two alternating narratives, set in Lancashire and London in 1977 and 1999. What follows is the beginning of the 1977 section.

Chapter One

Kate says one thing and I remember another, but in my own mind I know exactly how it started. We were in the dayroom with our mother. For a long time after I got there none of us spoke and nothing moved except the light, which kept vanishing and re-emerging in new patterns on the blank wall and buffed linoleum floor. Coming down the corridor the same white light had dazzled me, so that I looked away from it, sideways, into alcoves filled with monitors and machines, and at the swing door leading to a ward, which a nurse flicked open to reveal beds and a locker, blankets moulded to the shape of a body, a visitor walking away. Further on were lounges, where half-dressed patients sat staring at nothing or at loud little televisions balanced on trolleys. "Yes, Mr Jordan. That is correct," I heard from one. "That makes a total of twenty-two points," and walking on there was silence and space, and an old woman left alone, slipping in an armchair, eyes rolling, yellow nails grasping at bits of dust in the air. "Mr. Jordan, let's lift the screen and see what you've won," came dulled from behind an almost closed door, and then I turned a corner and, because it was darker, saw the floor separate out into grey hexagons on polished black. The heels of my high sandals clicked sharply against it.

According to my mother's directions I should have carried on, but when I looked up I saw a little girl sitting against the wall. She was rolling a coin forwards repeatedly, catching it each time it started to fall. She seemed absorbed, but looked up when she noticed me. I stopped in front of her and smiled. Her hair was almost waist length. It was darker than I remembered, almost brown now, though strands of blonde were still visible towards the front where her fringe had grown out and was fraying. There was a rash on her left cheek, and she was wearing a short blue dress, which made her seem thinner than she should have been.

"Hello Ellen," I said. She didn't react, and for a moment I thought it must be the wrong child. Then, looking at her again, I saw a clear resemblance to Kate. "I'm Anna," I said. "You remember me, don't you?" She backed away as I moved forward. "Are the others in there?" I asked, pointing at the door behind her. Her face didn't change; her eyes moved blankly across mine. Perhaps Stephen had been right, I thought. I shouldn't have come. Then, telling myself not to overreact, I remembered that I hadn't seen Ellen for almost four months. She was only just seven. Her mother was ill. I repeated the question, and when she still didn't answer I gave up and walked past her, into the room.

I stopped just inside the doorway. My mother was leaning against the window, staring out, and Kate was sitting slumped on a sofa. Neither of them noticed me. Kate's eyes were shut. She was still slim and her skin was clear but she was pale, and her hair, which was usually thicker than mine but the same dark brown, was greasy. Loose strands were clinging to her cheek; the tight knot which secured the rest of it had strained her forehead into rigid little lines. We had similar features but they didn't suit me. She sat up and her eyes met mine, then jerked away. I had intended to kiss her, but now that it came to it, I felt too awkward. Ellen came in and went to sit beside her, and she pulled her closer, pushing her lips hard against her head.

"You're in here," I said eventually. My mother turned round, blinking and trying to focus in the darker light of the room. She looked at me for a second or two, while her vision cleared, and then saw me and smiled.

"Oh, hello Anna," she said. "You found us then. Was the journey alright?"

I nodded. Kate lifted Ellen off her and stood up. She was wearing a white top, tighter than I would have chosen, and her trousers were slightly too long. The folds fell loosely around her ankles as she moved. I went towards her.

"How are you Kate?" I asked.

"Oh fine, fine." She smiled. "Bad headache though." She seemed composed, even friendly, but then something moved in her face and she said, "You've missed all the drama, though, Anna. You could've stayed at home."

I glanced at Ellen, who was pushing her fingers into the hole where the sofa was torn. When I looked back, my mother had moved away from the window. "I wanted to come," I said. "I wanted to help."

Kate shrugged. "That was nice of you."

"That's OK." A wave of heat spread over my face and chest.

In the corner behind me, I was conscious of my mother trying to distract Ellen. Did she want an ice cream? Would she come to the shop with her? "We can get a drink for Mummy as well," she said, her mouth etched into a smile, the rest of her face stiff. Ellen stood up, watching for Kate's approval. The hot plastic cover sucked free from the backs of her legs, leaving uneven red marks on her skin. Kate nodded, and Ellen let my mother take her hand. At the door they turned back.

"Orange juice is it, Kate?"

"If they've got it. Thanks."

We stood together and watched them go. I turned to Kate on impulse. "Listen Kate, I'm really sorry. I'm not surprised you're annoyed. I wish I'd been better on the phone, but Stephen was there and it was late – and I didn't realise things were quite so bad." I paused, conscious that I was making excuses. "The thing is, I really do just want to help. I know all this is partly my fault."

She looked straight at me. "What are you talking about?"

It was as though I was a long way off, trying to direct myself by remote control. I folded my arms. My body was limp and unwieldy. "I know I don't know enough about it. I'm not saying I do. I just feel terrible that you were so unhappy and I didn't help –"

"It was an accident, Anna." She moved closer to me, folding her arms so that we were facing each other in a mirror image.

"I didn't realise –" I said. "I thought –"

She turned away. "Come on Anna. You didn't seriously think I'd try to kill myself, did you? With Ellen in the flat?" Her voice was tight.

It would probably have been better to say nothing, but the way she was emphasising my name irritated me, and I launched into justifications: "It's just you sounded so fed up the other night, and then when Mum told me what happened –"

Kate's hair was coming down on one side. She sat in the nearest armchair and lifted her hands to it. "No, it's been hard, but not that bad," she said. Undoing the clip, shaking her hair loose, she was still watching me.

"I thought –" I checked myself again.

The clip was in her mouth, straight teeth visible as she coiled back her hair. Running my tongue over my own teeth, feeling for where they overlapped, I sat on the arm of the sofa. There was noise from the corridor: doors swinging; footsteps; a woman laughing; indistinct conversation, then silence. I willed my mother to hurry up.

Kate's hairclip clicked into place. "I know what you thought. I've been trying to tell Mum as well. I just drank too much. I forgot I'd already taken the sleeping pills so I had some more." She shook her head at me, half smiling. "I was drunk, Anna. It's fine. I'd have been alright anyway, that's the main thing."

I considered several responses and abandoned them all. "Good," I said eventually. "So you're going to the cottage then?"

She answered, but I didn't take it in. All the time she was talking I was thinking about what she'd just said. It didn't make sense. Before long, she stopped. She was standing up again, waiting for an answer, and I realised I had no idea what I was supposed to be reacting to. Groping back through my memory, I tried to reconstruct the sense of it, and it came to me that I'd asked her about the cottage. It was my mother's, left to her years before by an aunt. We had often visited it as children.

"I've just come from there actually," I said. "We walked round Esthwaite yesterday. Oh, and we got you some food as well," I added, picking up speed so she couldn't interrupt. "From the Co-op in Hawkshead. It's quite big, really, considering how small everything else is round there. I didn't know what sort of cereal you'd want, so I got a few kinds. At least you've got a choice then." Kate sat down again and leant back against the chair, watching me. She didn't react to anything I was saying, and I wondered whether it was obvious I hadn't been listening. But the only way to cover up was to carry on talking, and I was in the middle of some other pointless sentence when my mother and Ellen came back.

After we'd said goodbye, Ellen moved away reluctantly, glancing back at Kate. She didn't seem to see her, and Ellen was almost past the sofa when Kate reached for her waist and pulled her back. It was a half-hearted movement that seemed to stop before it was finished, so that Ellen was left leaning against her, her feet twisted at an angle on the carpet.

"You'll be OK while I'm at Mum's cottage won't you?" Kate asked her. "It won't be for long." Ellen nodded slowly, pushing her head against Kate's neck. I wanted to call to her to come away; I was desperate to get out of the hospital. Instead, I reached for the door, and stood holding it, waiting.

"I'll miss you," Kate said to Ellen. "A lot. You know I will, don't you?"

"Ellie'll be fine with Anna, though," my mother said smoothly. "It'll all be OK, just while you have a rest. I'll be here at ten o'clock tomorrow. That'll be about right, won't it?"

"I should think so." Kate followed us out of the room. "They reckon they can discharge me as soon as the doctor turns up." She put her hand on her daughter's head, parting the hair from the back with her fingers. "Bye, Ellie. I'll ring you soon." Ellen was silent. Kate kissed her again and then, because Ellen refused to continue until she was out of sight, we all watched her walk back down the corridor towards her ward.

Chapter Two

Some specific incidents from that first week stand out, but much of what comes to mind is indistinct. I remember particular sounds: a woman I never saw calling for her cat at dusk each evening; voices of children playing on the street. When I think of the afternoons, I see Ellen running barefoot up the fire-escape, her hair tangled, teeth parted, pausing to wipe her eye with her arm. Sometimes she stopped to talk to me, but usually she ran past, flinching if I tried to touch her.

Her mood changed constantly. There seemed to be no pattern to it. When her friends were with her she was alert and competitive, but alone with me she was often withdrawn, and I found it hard to gauge what she was really feeling. But there was one brief phase, when I'd been there a few days, when she was particularly talkative, telling me about the Jubilee Day parties she'd been to at the beginning of the month and showing me the photograph of the costume she'd worn for a fancy-dress competition at school. She was wearing a red mackintosh, a straw hat and wellington boots covered in ribbons and tin foil, holding an umbrella. Strapped across her shoulders was a cardboard placard announcing '25 years rain!' She'd won a prize, she said, but in the background there were other girls in crowns, coloured dresses and robes, and I couldn't help thinking that her costume wouldn't have taken long to make, and that the gesture was entirely typical of Kate.

The flat itself was at the top of a semi-detached sandstone house. The building had obviously been spacious once, but now it had been cut up into six small apartments. Kate had lived here for more than a year, but to me it felt as though she'd only just moved in. A pile of clothes was heaped underneath a chair in her hall, and beside it were several boxes, still full of books. There was very little furniture. When we'd first come back from the hospital, I'd looked round the living room, taking it all in. Opposite the two-bar electric fire, a worn sofa squatted on bent metal legs. A narrow table stood by the window, its top entirely covered with loose papers, ashtrays and cups. At the edge, plants were balanced on a pile of books, leaning towards the light. The air was humid, dense with the smell of stale cigarette smoke.

I sat on the sofa and my mother put her bag down beside me. "Right then, Anna, shall I make some tea?"

"Please," I said. "Do you want some help?" She shook her head, gesturing to me not to get up.

"I'll help you," Ellen said. "It's best the way we have it anyway." It was the first thing I'd heard her say that day, and I noticed that she had obvious traces of the local accent, stressing some consonants and skipping others, rounding the ends of words into the wrong shape. Last time I'd seen her it had been much less pronounced.

"I thought you said you didn't like tea," my mother said to her.

"I never. I'm always having it." She disappeared through the doorway behind me, back into the kitchen. My mother followed. "I don't think there's any teabags, are there?" I heard her say from the kitchen.

Ellen laughed. "There might be some at the back of the cupboard. Kate and me use leaves, though." Her voice continued in the distance, confident, with an implausible, slightly condescending edge.

The smell of smoke was oppressive. I leant across the table and loosened the lock on the sash-window, pushing at the lower half until I managed to make it lurch up a few inches. Standing back, I noticed that my hands were covered in a thin dust, which stuck to my palms when I tried to brush it off. Outside, an aeroplane was moving between the roofs of the houses opposite, leaving effervescent streaks in the sky. I watched them fade, resolving to do everything I could to help Ellen. It was obvious Kate had let things get out of control.

L ooking out that evening, at about eight o'clock, I saw a group of teenagers congregating outside the flats opposite. There were five boys, all in their mid-teens, leaning against the wall that separated a communal garden from the street. One had a shaved head and boots; one a leather jacket. At first glance, the others were indistinguishable. Two girls were standing in front of them, with their backs to me. The taller, in tight blue jeans, with fair hair loose across her denim jacket, was slightly closer to the boys. As I watched she leant forward to let one of them light her cigarette. Someone offered her the bottle they'd been passing between them. She laughed as the boy beside her tried to wrestle it away, kicking him with the edge of her sandals, staggering back into the road as he pushed at her. He took hold of her shoulders and she twisted away from him, giggling, inhaling on her cigarette. A car came towards them and they backed off onto the pavement, where she passed the bottle on to her friend, who was waiting awkwardly behind her.

I turned to Ellen. She was sitting at the table in her dressing gown, eating cornflakes. Her left leg was bent under her body and a book was propped against a cup in front of her. Once, when the group outside started to laugh she lifted herself up to look across at them. "Who are they?" I asked.

"I don't know."

I moved closer to her. "But have you seen them before? Do they live near here?"

She nodded. Looking back at the window, thinking for a moment, she pointed and said, "Them ones do anyway."

"Those ones," I said, but I was reassured. They were obviously local kids, not likely to be threatening.

They were there again a few nights later, then absent for about a week. I didn't worry about them then. They were simply a disturbance, typical of the area in which Kate had chosen to live.

When I started to explore the next day, I soon realised that as long as we didn't walk too far in any one direction it would be impossible to get lost. The town had been built over a series of hills. In the centre it was almost level, but where Kate lived the streets were stacked above each other, intersecting at sharp angles. If we went uphill when we wanted to go home, we were bound to come out close to her flat.

We walked to the end of the street, turned left onto a wider road lined with redbrick terraced houses, and went on, past several small shops. A group of young women in saris and headscarves were laughing outside a house. On the opposite side, the ground swelled into a grassy mound. "What's that?" I asked Ellen.

"The coalies."

"The –" I made her repeat it, but still didn't know what she meant. "What is it though?"

"I don't know." She looked uncomfortable. "I think it's for getting coal out."

"They used to be mines, you mean?"

She shrugged, half-nodding, obviously unsure.

We crossed the road. Steep concrete paths had been layered into the earth, twisting around the knoll to converge at the summit. Even walking quickly, it took a few minutes to reach the top. As soon as it evened out we stopped, both slightly out of breath. To the left, hills soon cut off the view, but looking straight ahead it stretched out, flat, for miles. Past the church, the schools and the rows of houses were mills, clustered together, distinguishable by their tall brick chimneys with names embedded round them in white. I started to count them, and gave up at thirty-five. In the distance, roads spread in loose patterns to the cramped buildings and towers of the city, thinning out to the countryside beyond. I stepped off the path and forward onto the grass, noticing that it was already yellowing among patches of dry soil.

"The view's amazing." I turned to Ellen, laughing, almost excited.

Her smile was proprietorial. "Kate and me like it here too."

"Is it Manchester?"

She nodded. "You can't see that much of Oldham from here." She pointed to the right. "Over there's the park though."

"Where?"

"You can't see it from here but it's there." She swung her arm round. "There's where Kate works."

"Next to it?"

"No, there." She pointed straight ahead, to the verdigris spires of a large building, surrounded by car parks and playing fields. "At the end of the big road."

"That's what I meant. It's obvious that's a school."

She took a few steps away and didn't answer, suddenly absorbed in the patterns her foot made scraping against the ground. I left her for a few minutes, then called to her. "Ellie, don't do that to your shoes." They were new. My mother had bought them for her recently. Ellen didn't look up. The side of her shoe dragged back loose stones and soil, and when she straightened it, I saw that the leather was lined with small scratches. "Come on," I said. "Show me where your school is." She glanced at me, and then away. Her movements were less confident. "Please, Ellen, I'll need to know. Is it there?" I gestured randomly towards the city. "Is that where we've got to go tomorrow?"

Her eyes moved across my face. "You know it isn't."

"Isn't it?" I smiled. "I thought it was. Show me then."

"I'm not a baby."

"I know, but – I thought that was it." I indicated a large building. She was standing stiffly, her hands by her sides, waiting for me to stop pretending. "Is it there then?" I said finally, nodding to the smaller school we had passed just down the road. We could see the back wall, the playground, the clock tower. She nodded. "It looks nice," I said. As we went across to the path and started to walk back down the hill, I risked putting a hand on her shoulder. She didn't move it away.

"There's two gates," she said spontaneously as we rounded the first corner and chose the path which led back to the road. "One for infants, and one for juniors."

"And are you an infant?" I asked, before I could catch myself. I waited for her to object, to point out that I knew exactly how old she was, but it didn't seem to occur to her.

"Next year I'm a junior," she said.

"And do the infants and juniors share the same playground?"

"No, we have one and they have one."

At the end of the path, just before it met the pavement, I drew Ellen to one side to let a young couple pass. They were both about sixteen, in trainers and jeans. The girl was holding the boy's arm, the breeze blowing her hair forward onto her face. He was wearing a leather jacket, with the collar turned up. As they passed, he nodded to Ellen. The girl glanced at me, momentarily surprised. I looked at Ellen. She was still smiling.

"Do you know him?" I asked.

"He goes to Kate's school."

"Oh." I thought about it. "Does that girl go there too?"

"I don't know." We walked onto the pavement and stopped opposite the primary school to cross the road. Cars were coming towards us, and while we waited for them to go by I looked back over my shoulder. The couple had chosen the lowest path, and were walking away from us. As I watched, they paused, kissed briefly, and went on out of sight.

Ellen pulled at my hand. "We can go now."

"Do you know lots of the kids from Kate's school?"

I thought that she hesitated, slightly. "Some of them."

We walked back the way we'd come, then turned onto a wider street lined with trees. Gradually, the terraces turned into semi-detached houses with gardens, then they were stone, set back and concealed from the road by walls and long lawns. We crossed the road and turned into the park. The path sloped down steeply, but the grass on either side eventually evened out into a flat field. In the distance, the city was still visible. To our right were several small greenhouses, obviously open to the public. I thought of suggesting that we should go to see the plants, but it was suddenly windy and though it was still warm I noticed clouds gathering above us as we walked down towards the playground.

"We've picked the wrong time," I said. "It's going to rain. Everyone's leaving." Two women were walking away from the roundabout, one fussing with the hood of a pushchair as she went. A child stared out at us from beneath the blue canvas; another walked next to it, holding onto the handle. The women stopped by the gate and shouted to an older boy to hurry.

"Are we going home too?" Ellen asked.

"Not straight away. It's up to you. We can wait a bit," I said.

"I'm not bothered." Her face was still and pale. We were standing by the gate of the playground. The swings rocked gently in the wind, dropping forwards at different speeds. From time to time the roundabout twisted a few inches one way and then back against itself

"Let's go then," I said impatiently. She followed me back onto the road. Before we had reached the pavement the tarmac ahead was dotted with rain. We walked quickly up the hill towards Kate's flat. A car passed us but otherwise the streets were empty. "We'd better get you changed when we get home," I said when we were nearly there. "We don't want you getting ill." Ellen looked at me frowning, resolutely silent.

For a little while after that, the days seem to merge into each other, but I remember that we were in the baker's one afternoon that week. It must have been about three o'clock, one of the first days I'd picked Ellen up from school. The shop was full when we got there. We went across the road to buy the evening paper, but there was still a queue when we got back. Service was slow. I glanced over every now and then, to check on Ellen, who'd wandered out through the open door. When I first looked, she was leaning against a little wall, looking down at her new shoes. The straw hat she'd insisted on wearing that day was dangling across her back from a loose loop of elastic, which was hanging from the flesh of her lower lip. She had tied her cardigan round her waist and it dipped untidily over her shorts. One cuff trailed to the ground behind her. Across the street a woman was painting the frame above her open door. Further away a radio was playing music half-muted.

I moved forwards in the queue, counting out loose change. Ellen was stretching her hat elastic out in front of her, holding it steady with both hands. One of the women looked up from wrapping the bread and followed my eyes.

"Isn't that Kate Martin's little girl?"

"Yes." It occurred to me that she might have heard about the ambulance. I tried to maintain an ambivalent tone. "My niece."

"Oh." There was a short silence. I was conscious of the other woman turning to look at me. "That's fourteen pence, please. – Oh you've got the change? Lovely." The coins had stuck to my hand. I rubbed it against my jacket. "So Mrs Martin's not teaching at the school any more then?"

"She'll be back before long." My eyes met hers, as blank as I could make them.

"Lovely day," she said, and I looked at the window again and saw wide glass shelves, now almost empty, the huge window pane, the circular photograph of a woman biting into a cream cake, and then Ellen, standing on the pavement outside. As I put my purse away I dropped a coin and bent to find it, flustered, just registering that Ellen was talking to a man. Fair hair. The coin was by my foot. Standing up, I took the bread from the woman, forcing it down into my plastic bag. The bread bulged uncomfortably through the flimsy handles. I took the newspaper out and pinned it to my body with my elbow.

Outside, Ellen was standing against the wall, just as I had first seen her from the shop. Her head was tilted up towards the sun. She opened her eyes as I approached and pulled the hat back onto her head. The elastic dropped down beneath her chin. "At last!"

I shifted a bag from one hand to the other so that I could take her arm. "Ellie, don't chew that elastic."

"I wasn't."

"No, but you were before. You might choke."

"I won't." She stared up, aggrieved.

"You might." I let a few seconds pass. "By the way, who was that you were talking to before?"

"No one." She said it quickly. I watched her carefully, but her face didn't change. "No one," she repeated. "I've not talked to anyone at all." She took the newspaper out from under my arm, and we walked back down the hill in silence.

CATHY ROSARIO

from *Wave*

Cathy Rosario grew up in Keele. She has worked for several years as a writer and other things in England, Jamaica, The Philippines, Italy and India. The novel she is currently writing is a darkly comic romance set in a Filipino mountain city. It is called *Wave*. The action revolves around three pairs of would-be lovers.

Prologue

Ruth felt someone's eyes on her. She turned and there was the woman with the baby. She wore the maroon uniform of a government worker. The woman twisted her neck to see her baby's face.

"Ooo, he likes you. Look how he's staring. Yes, it's a white lady." She stroked the tall, fluffy ears on his rabbit hat. She leant forward and across to Ruth. Her movements were so sharp and fast that she seemed to be set at a different speed to the rest of the passengers.

"You know my little Berto has just gone through a crucial stage. Yes. Before, everything – I mean everything – he just wants to eat, to put in his mouth. There was only one consciousness in the world – only one," she held up a manicured finger, "and that was his. Everything else," she waved her hand over the passengers on the jeepney, "was just here for him to eat. But now – and this is a most crucial stage – now," she lowered her voice "he wants to communicate." She leant back. "O, yes. He wants to reach out to other consciousnesses. He loves to wave. Don't you Berto?" She looked down at him. "Wave to the lady."

The baby carried on staring. Ruth wondered if the woman had been a bit premature in her assessment. She knew that expression in his eyes. She saw it in the Balthazars' faces when they settled down for dinner. The baby was looking at her as though she were edible. His long ears quivered. Ruth felt her armpits prick with sweat.

"Wave to the nice lady, Berto," the woman demanded again. By now the other passengers were sat tense with anticipation.

"Wave now," said the woman.

The baby waved. He stared right at Ruth and waved. The passengers dissolved into indulgent smiles. He waved again, this time frantically. His mouth fell open in excitement. His ears waggled. Before Ruth's eyes came a vision of the baby with his teeth clamped on her arm.

"Wave," the woman said to Ruth. "Wave." She shaped her lips around the word.

Ruth had never realised it had so many syllables. She couldn't move. The other passengers stared at her with a kind of dread.

"Wave!" hissed the old woman sat to Ruth's left, and her tattooed hand clenched Ruth's knee. "Wave!"

The Waterlogged City

The droning. If you judge by innovation, it is wanting. This is music to take a shaman into his trance. But the shaman had gone, being old and bemused by this gathering and riled by the disparaging remarks of the anthropologist, who was old as well and had forgotten herself. So it was left to the artists to dance, in sharp birdlike plunges, their arms outstretched, flicking up their hands as though they were wings. Hamog artists do not just paint: they are also musicians, poets, dancers, the Renaissance men of this small mountain city. The fire had dried and swollen the skins of the drums, but still Hamog's sodden surface held in the thinness of the gong's clang. Listeners got up stiffly when Ferdie the chef appeared, damp hair sticking to his face, the kitchen heat shining on his cheeks and his apron bloodied. "Mangan tayon. Let's eat – again." He grinned as he watched the people on their way to his food laid out in the dark garden.

Behind them Poly called for light and when nothing happened dashed off to the kitchen. He was the manager here at Ipu-Ipo. When Napoleon and Socrates De Souza first came to Hamog from Manila and named this wooden, gabled house Ipu-Ipo, there were dark mutterings about the folly of such a name, because it means typhoon. True, the house had stood for almost a hundred years and had even retained many of its original stained glass windows, but it doesn't do to tempt fate.

As Soc never tired of telling people, the house had been an excellent purchase. It had been built for an American functionary, who had lived there at the turn of the century. Its position in the highest part of Hamog, and its dense perimeter wall of bamboo, gave it the feel of a lofty eyrie, protected from the dirt and clamour beyond its gates. It offered a leafy haven for the birds that had all but deserted the hungry city. Converting the house to suit the De Souzas' purposes had been simple enough. The two high-ceilinged reception rooms were ideal for the gallery and the book and gift shop, and the first floor offered ample living quarters for the two brothers. The only work required was to build a café. There had been a fraught few weeks when Soc's desire for ostentation had quite got the better of his keen business sense, and he had set his heart on having the café built in the style of a Greek temple, although obviously scaled down. All Poly's wiles and pleadings couldn't sway him from the idea. But the architect that Soc chose managed with great tact to steer him towards something far more simple. He pointed out that what Manila tourists really hanker after when they come to Hamog is to relive their own lost Arcadia. Soc reluctantly accepted this.

Before Soc could change his mind, the architect had the outer wall of the kitchen knocked down, and an open-walled structure built out from it, with a roof of thick, yellow thatch. On the lawn outside, he had a fireplace built within a circle of flat stones. While still on a roll, he bought an indigenous house from a Bontoc tribesman, had it dismantled and transported to Hamog, and adapted it into a gazebo. The original house had been raised from the ground on intricately carved stilts, around which black stone rings were fixed to keep the rats from climbing up. By some ingenious reworking, the architect used these stilts as supports for the gazebo's rattan walls, and preserved intact the distinctive four-sided thatched roof. The floorboards, hewn at a time when the ancient pine forests still existed, served as magnificent table-tops for the café. Soc knew it all made sense. He consoled himself by buying a huge mahogany table, which had enough grapes, vases and cupids carved on its hefty legs to soothe the most vulgar of hearts.

It was around this table that the guests now queued for their food. Only occasions such as this warranted it being carried out from its storage place in the cellar – a manoeuvre that required four strong men. The trapdoor of the cellar was the only door through which the cumbersome beast fitted. Soc had purchased it from a house auction in Manila, and his frequent boast was that it had been with the De Souzas since the early Spanish period. And so it had, although it was the more illustrious branch of the family. But fortunes come and go, and the original owners of the table had fallen on hard times.

Alice ladled meat and black gravy from the cauldron and looked down the table.

"Here you have, appearing out of the gloom in reverse order – tofu in peanut sauce, watercress and orange salad, some other poncey stuff and – great lumps of pig." She turned round to Ruth, the only other English woman at this mainly Filipino gathering. "Look at the fat on that." Ruth peered over and stumbled against one of the table's portly, clawed feet sunk into the sodden grass. A spray of water wet her ankles. Ruth, in her sandals and thin skirt, had still not got used to how quickly the temperature dropped once night fell. Alice, she noticed, also had bare legs beneath her short, velvet dress, but her feet were snugly encased in purple Doc Marten boots.

"Move along, Alice," said Ester from six back.

"Easy, tiger. I'm moving."

Alice and Ruth took their plates towards the gazebo, which tonight had its entrance decked with black curtains. Outside the gazebo, the architect had arranged the remainder of the fireplace stones into an informal seating area, under the narra tree.

"Lights, camera, action!" called Ferdie, and Ruth reared at the great shadows and brightness thrown across her path. A sweet potato slipped from her plate. She looked down at the lit grass, quickly stooped to pick the potato up, and then followed Alice. Alice sat down on the stones, with her plump, pale legs sprawled out in front of her. She forked in several mouthfuls and, her lips gleaming with fat, returned to her tale.

"So there I was – totally out of my head – and the taxi refuses to go any further. Thanks a lot mate. Out I get and start walking down the track. I find the steps going down to the house, but I walk a few paces, and then I'm confused. The steps aren't there anymore. I turn round to try again but all I can see is mud. It's so light because of the full moon, and all I can see is mud and the roof of the house below me. So I just start wading down anyhow. I lose one Welly, then the other, and I'm thinking I've entered the twilight zone and I never told mother I loved her – hey up, she's off, fancy telling the shaman how to interpret the pig's bile. Cheeky cow." Alice watched the old, Danish anthroplogist walk out through the gate. "Anyway, I at last find –" There were howlings from the artists again, reaching their climax, and Ruth felt the briefest moment of exhilaration. She puzzled over where she had heard that sound before. Then it came to her. It was the men on Hamog's building sites, howling down at her. But now, now, she was with the men, throwing back her head, beating through the green forest. O, Lord, what was Alice saying? Something about crashing out. Did Alice make it home then? Or did she find another doorway, or did she sleep out there in the sea of mud? Ruth listened. No, it sounded like Alice found her house.

"When I wake," said Alice, "it's morning. The rain's hitting the window as usual and there's about ten people outside, with bin bags over them, digging away. I feel like an Egyptian mummy, I've got that much dried mud on me. So I creak over to the window and ask what happened. 'Landslide. It'll be the house next time,' one of them says. So that's very comforting, isn't it? There's great cracks in the ceiling as it is. My landlady keeps going on about her firm foundations. Frankly, I doubt it. They can't even plumb a toilet properly here. I mean have you ever found one that flushes? It's always a bucket job. Still at least the rains have stopped."

Alice looked expectantly at Ruth.

"It has been very wet," said Ruth finally.

Her eyes moved shyly away from Alice's face up to her short, bright hair, then down to her plate. She thought she heard Alice give a small, impatient sigh, before spearing another piece of pork. They had only just met and Ruth was finding herself cowed to her usual silence.

Ruth had been in Hamog for just two weeks and it was only in the last four days that the rains had stopped. The mist had lifted to reveal the cramped city, with its teetering houses and ladders of steps cut out of the mountain sides. Without the great tree-root systems to hold the water, the rains had beaten down the bare mountain slopes, flooding the houses in the lowest valleys. The typhoon winds had bent and broken the sparse trees and blown apart the highest houses, ripping up their breeze blocks and corrugated iron roofs. Ruth had watched Hamog's citizens begin the familiar task of rebuilding their fragile homes, and drying out their possessions. She walked past furniture set out beneath the sun. It was not so much their being outside that had worried Ruth, but how things were arranged: a stiff-backed chair set too far away to reach the table, an armchair baring its stained, hessian base, a drawerless chest of drawers blocking the wire-mesh hatch of a chicken coop.

Now that the rains had stopped, this gathering to commemorate the first anniversary of Simon Ta-ins's death could be held, although a little late. Since Simon, like many of the artists here, had been from one of the Cordillera tribes, it had to be marked by a Canao, and the De Souza brothers gamefully produced a pig of monumental proportions to be ritually speared and butchered. Simon had been a Kalinga. They were known as the warrior tribe for the fury with which they fought attempts to log and dam and mine their land.

Ruth chased a slither of avocado around her plate. She wondered how old Alice was. Certainly younger than her; she looked barely in her twenties. She watched Alice's hands as they moved busily above her plate, and got a glimpse of the tender skin of her left wrist. She winced at the sight of the celtic design tattooed over Alice's dark veins.

"I thought it was a bracelet when I first saw you," said Ruth, pointing at it, and then, "Did it hurt?"

Alice laughed. "Yeah, like hell," she said. "Still, you got to be brave."

Brave? thought Ruth. Yes, I suppose so. She saw Ester and her husband Dominic walking towards them, and felt relieved. Warm, kind Ester. She wasn't so sure about Dominic; he seemed a bit morose. She had only met them in the last few days, when they had come to deliver organic vegetables to Ipu-Ipo.

"So still no Vince, ha?" asked Dominic, as he arranged himself on the stones and set his plate on his knees.

"Nope. He's not going out much at the moment. I don't know why," said Alice.

Ruth half-listened. Vince's name didn't mean anything to her yet. She looked at Dominic. He had bad skin, scarred by acne, but from the dullness of his face shone incongruously clear eyes. When Ruth had first moved into her cheap, long-stay hotel here in Hamog, she had opened the wardrobe door and found a mirror inside, opaque with dust. With her finger she had scored a line across it, and her eyes had shone out at her so suddenly that she had had to catch her breath. It was like that with Dominic's eyes.

"What's that on your plate Dominic? Meat?" said Alice.

"Observant as ever, Alice." Dominic looked embarrassed and rubbed his hand over his pitted cheek. "I've decided to make an exception for Canaos. Because it's totally different. No, don't look like that Ester. It is. You mestizos don't understand." Ester's grandfather was Spanish, a legacy that Ester was fond of saying had left her with nothing but a long nose and hairy legs. "It's honouring life," Dominic continued, "the great cycles of nature. Being born and returning to the earth. There's respect here for the pig's gift of its own life. Now, among us Pala'wans –" Ester snorted but Dominic pressed on, "It doesn't leave you Ester, I'm still a Pala'wan even if I was born in Manila. We believed – believe – that if someone becomes ill, it's because they or their kin have transgressed by taking too much from the earth. Maybe they have hunted too many of one animal so the spirit of that species is angry. And then it's up to the shaman to intervene and ask for the person's life to be returned. That's respect isn't it? And I see the same respect here amongst the Cordillera tribes."

"My dear," said Ester. "In the barrios people get into debt just so they can throw a lavish Canao. I'm afraid all the butchering is more about impressing the neighbours than honouring nature. Now what's Poly's problem?"

Poly walked up to them, nervous and gabbling. "Have any of you seen Yason? I can't find him. Is this a good idea? The boy's brilliant but will he be appreciated here? I just want Yason to tell me what he's going to do. He's so – close about it."

This was the kind of gathering where dress was unconventional with a strong leaning towards long hair, tattoos and beads. Most people, if asked, would insist that there was no dress code and believe it. But the newcomer Yason – in his calf-length pleated skirt, brogues, and shawl held in place by a cameo brooch – had created a certain unease.

"I saw him a bit ago by the café, mumbling away. Perhaps going over his lines?" said Alice.

Dominic touched Poly's knee. "Poly, I've been trying to convince Ferdie to have one of my solar cookers. It's a perfect place here but I just can't get through to him –"

"It's all in the timing," called back Poly, setting off at full trot.

At that moment, Yason peered out of the gazebo from behind the black curtains, wearing a Chinese rice farmer's hat. "The performance of 'Yo! Simon, we've not forgotten you' is about to begin," he announced. "There is room for ten people in the gazebo. Ten people only."

"Not yet Yason," Poly cried, running back and pushing his way through the curtains. The artists were only just getting their food and others were hovering for second helpings.

"You know he's got a coffin in there," said Dominic disapprovingly," and a bucket of pig's blood. I don't know what kind of vibes this is going to give our vegetables, Ester. It could well put people off buying them from there. What was Poly thinking of? Everyone loved Simon. His death's still raw. And Yason never even met him. He's not even from these parts. It could go down very badly. Very badly indeed." Dominic shook his head.

Ester looked at the gazebo. "Poly's not come out".

Several other people were also looking over curiously.

"Let's see what's going on," said Alice. All four of them cautiously approached the gazebo, Ruth trailing last.

Alice put her ear to the curtain.

"I can hear a typewriter," she whispered.

"Have a look," urged Ester.

Alice hesitated a moment longer then pulled the curtain aside.

They saw Poly crouched on the ground. He looked up as the curtain moved and gave them a little resigned shrug. Yason did not appear to notice them. He was bent over his typewriter, tapping out a letter with two fingers, a lit candle and telephone at his side. Strewn about him, on the table and in the coffin that filled most of the floor-space, were screwed-up airmail envelopes and typewritten letters. Poly beckoned to them and they filed in. Ruth picked her way over the tree-roots that knotted the ground at the doorway of the gazebo. She edged around the end of the coffin. At that moment, Yason gave a gusty groan, and the candle flame spluttered. Ruth drew back and lost her balance. Her arms wheeled in the air as the coffin lurched towards her. She pulled back, slipped on a root, and took a nose dive into the coffin.

Ruth lay still, her face pressed into the rose satin upholstery, too ashamed to move. She noted dimly that she'd bashed her shin and it felt like she'd pulled a muscle in her neck. Her arms and legs splayed over the wooden sides. It seemed you had to lie in an orderly manner to fit inside a coffin.

Ester bent over to haul her up. "Are you all right, dear?" she whispered. She looked almost as distressed as Ruth. Ruth nodded. She could see a dark patch of damp on the satin where her mouth had been.

Throughout all this, Yason did not stir from his work.

They sat down in a row. Alice reached for a letter, and held it at an angle so the paper caught the candle light. It was from Simon to Ryan Gallery in New Zealand. "Dear Steph. No, certainly I have still some hope to be there for my exhibition. But you know how they say it is good to have a Plan b? Even if you are James Bond, di ba? And, to be truthful, lately I have not been feeling too bionic. The photos you sent and the map are perfect, and you write how the light is falling so precisely. I feel as though I am even there. No bola. Bola? Aray, I am such a native that I cannot write a sentence in English without wanting to slip in a Filipino word. What I mean to say is no kidding. Anyway, to return to the matter in hand, I have marked on the map where I want my paintings to hang. I know, I know – I am too zealous. Such awkward creatures we are."

Ester looked over Alice's shoulder. "He finally had to agree he was too sick to make it," she whispered. "Where on earth did Yason get these letters from?"

Ruth looked at them sat with their knees against their chins. She saw Dominic's eyelids begin to droop. Alice yawned, and her eyes watered. The yawn ran through the others. How can they be so calm, thought Ruth, in this reek of blood? I shouldn't be here. It wasn't my choice to come to this place. Yason lifted the bail of the typewriter and took out his letter. He read it, then screwed it up and dropped it on the floor. Carefully, he inserted another piece of paper and resumed typing. Dominic's head drifted down to Ester's shoulder, his jaw slack. Ruth saw Yason pick up the phone. He swished out of the gazebo.

"Eh?" said Dominic.

"Um, shall we follow?" suggested Poly.

Outside, a crowd had gathered and was watching Yason as he moved weakly amongst them, the loose wire of the phone pressed in his left ear and holding the receiver to his right. After two circuits of the lawn, he returned to the gazebo, pulled open the curtains and climbed into the coffin. One more muttered conversation, then he put down the phone, pulled off his hat, shawl and sweater and reached for the bucket of pig's blood. Scooping up blood in both hands, he smeared it over his bare torso, his face and hair. There was a general jostling among the audience for a good view. Ruth stood between Poly and Alice.

The blood was bright and held darker clots. Yason began what sounded like an incantation but as his voice rose, it became clear he was reciting Simon's hospital bills. Then, trilling through the litany of examinations, drugs, chemotherapy, laundry and food, came the beep of a cellular phone. Socrates reached for his jacket pocket. "Hello? …Ah Joel. Kumusta ka? You not shut up shop yet? That's what I like, talaga! Committed employees, ha?" Soc bellowed with laughter. "So that's why you're phoning, ha? So I know?" More bellows. Then his expression became serious. "Oo

– Sino? What he's there now? Ah Apo. Noong nakausap ko siya, sinabi ko ha di puwerde ang mag-credit – not after last time. Cash only. He can't hear us can he? O, hoops …Okay ngayon? Aiee naku. These people di ba? Always after credit."

"Soc." Poly looked pleadingly into his brother's seamed and bloated face. Ruth found it hard to believe that there was only eight years between them. Poly's nervous movements and wide, naïve eyes quite belied his forty-nine years. Ruth had only just started working for the De Souzas, but she was already clear that Socrates was to be avoided whenever possible. Poly had told her that Soc spent a lot of his time at his computer shops in Manila. She remembered Poly's laugh when he had seen the pleased look she'd been unable to hide.

"What?" said Soc to Poly.

"Nakaka disturb ka ng performance," whispered Poly.

"O, that's what you call it?"

Ester took a firm hold of Soc's arm and steered him round to the art gallery side of the house.

"Joel?" said Soc down the phone. "For a while, ha? … Aray Ester!"

"Where did Yason get this stuff from, Poly?" whispered Alice, leaning over Ruth.

"He asked Simon's brother." His voice taut, he pointed in the Filipino way with his lips.

Alice looked over to where the brother stood with their father. Both their faces were impassive as they listened to Yason. Others glanced at them as well, the palely gleaming faces of the foreigners looking particularly worried.

Yason stopped. He began to smile and wave, looking out with myopic eyes at the crowd. Everybody tensed.

"O, Apo," said Dominic to Alice. "That was Simon. He left the hospital to die at home. He'd sit in the doorway in his wheelchair." He swallowed. "People seeing him they stared. He was so thin you see. And he just gave them that smile he had and waved. They'd find themselves waving back." His eyes filled with tears.

There was a sharp intake of breath from the crowd as Simon's father stepped forward.

"Come on lad," he said. "Get that blood off you and put on some warm clothes or you'll be following poor Simon to his grave." He spoke kindly, in Ilocano, a language the Manila-born Yason did not know.

Yason turned towards the voice, squinting through the darkness. "Salamat po," he said softly. That is: thank you.

OLIVER SHELLEY

Nine Poems

Oliver Shelley grew up near Oxford and now lives in Cambridge. He is currently working on his first collection of poems.

Frances

Days into your illness, my patience ending,
the toilet flooded and you came to watch.
"That's the cause;" you said, pointing your finger,
"slack water breeding poor air, a blockage. "
No Frances, the house was sour – too breath-warm
with our stillness. There was something on our love,
some slow blight that had crept over time
and now lay in the stone, lay in the hearth.
Frances, how could we hope to stay well there?
It had taken root, it was wounding us.

And my distance was also a steady taint
that had worked itself into me and thrived.
I came to see how lukewarm we were: our skin
was not tight, our kisses were only soft;
all our clamour had been taken by settling.
Frances, I was dreaming of salt and limes,
of the black sand beaches and cypress groves
where we burnt and each kiss was a sear.
But when I woke the sheets were damp and flat
from your night sweats in that final Autumn.

I could not sleep. The moon at the curtains
and your heat made me rise. A night of storms:
the roof already caught, the hedges bound,
the angles of the house sharpened by air.
And seven white gulls landed on the grass.
They squatted below the cove of the wall,
each of them separate, facing the wind,
sleek in its pressing and held to the lawn.
But when you turned on the light they rose up,
staggered in the hard wind and were soon lost.

Polar Bears

They don't take in the concrete icebergs,
the wilted tundra or the litter in their pond,
but mat themselves together in sadness
as they pace out their forecourt in pairs.
Instinct makes them move; their heads
pitch with each lope and twin reel
like iron lamps swung in a breeze.
They have cut down their act to this dance
and will circle until their gaze has spun
something like snow-glare from their confinement:
to sleep without calling to the Pole Star,
the close bark of seals stirring nothing in their blood.

Magpies

Two magpies harried the new cat,
circling between the roof and the birch.
They took turns to press him to the lawn
with only the wind in the fruit cages
to put them off their wheel.
But it was shame that kept him down:
he knew I had seen his first patrol
stolen by the cuff and heckle
of these swaggering birds.
So I shot one of them in the head
as it paused on the stump of a yew:
its spine kicked back like a broken book,
the jib-tail flipped it over like a lid.

For hours now the mate has stayed
cursing this house for its sorrow
and I see how the murder will grow.
My cat has found his legs but squats
in the shade of a fir. His eyes are fixed
on the nests above and his blood-mewl
is lost in the din: across the garden,
every parent butting at the grief to come
as my accomplice begins to ascend.

Two Horses

As each bomb fell,
their spines convulsed,
and their eyes began to flare.

They set their heads up wind;
the stench made them reel,
veins strung tight in their necks.

The trucks drew near
and they pressed themselves together
until ribs engaged;

each wrought breath
locked the joint only tighter.
And then they waited;

the ground beaten,
the air marked black,
to be undone.

Crop

Land hemmed by water and hedges
where the horizon has grown vague
with the steady line it draws
and the black stitch of these rails
runs machine-straight as a scar.
My grandmother spent her life
in open fields and drills like these,
collecting beet from the plough's turn
and hurling each one to the heap;
they gathered there bleeding
and steamed in the glare of the sun.
In winter, plugged down in boots
cut from car tyres, she left at dawn
to pick loose coal by the track side.
She worked along each road bed,
scouring her hands on the shale,
for knotted fists of clinker
that gave out the last of their glow
and then sank, inert, in the grate.
But the best crop came near the border,
by the side of the tunnel's mouth;
the held air raked coal from the hod
of freight trains that left in the night.

Grandfather

Our grandfather by the sea, blind.
His deck chair settles our rug on the stones
and his face takes sunlight like thirst.
We always play games that need speaking;
each of our cards and moves are told
and he smiles in his taking part.
We are saying our childhood to this old man
and his beautiful face, liver-marked and shy,
has no end in its space, no end in its gentleness,
to hold a whole life of listening left to do.

Pass

That afternoon, when we were young,
I went from shop to shop looking,
willing you to step out into the sun
and to smile at me so that we could start.
The town was so full I was sure that it had you
held in the drive of an aisle or a door
but everyone turned out not to be you
and hoping had made me tired.

And you had been waiting in my garden,
my mother drawing you from the window.
She filled pages as you sat, held in the light,
she fixed that time. Until the air turned;
the wasps came to the vine,
the roses took to their scent in the evening's change.

Still

The whole of the water's stillness comes from its depth.
He has the boat at that point of the lake
where the darkness runs like a tether down,
like a coil drawn still by the weight below.

And the coil of his thoughts,
held taut by loss and change,
grows quiet in the same way.
Breathing softens, his eyes take light.
This calm comes to the lake and the trees;
the bank has settled at the shore,
the reeds entwine and stay.

And then, with some flight in the air,
the rain moves over once more, slow and complete,
and he takes it to him as a gesture, he takes on time.
He has his watch on his wrist.
The boat shifts a little on its seam
and there is no end in the leaf of the water.

Christmas in the Commonwealth

They have stopped talking in far continents.
The anthem runs like a creek to its end
and old men stand on islands to listen,
squinting against either sun or snow
as birds fly past in any way to warmth.
Many things change, she says, but we must talk,
we must bring ourselves together for hope
and each pause holds silence over the world.

But close by, the message has become weak;
I'm trying to catch it, to tune to that hope,
but I think that this household is broken:
my husband silent, bitter in the lounge,
my parents talking to each other like guests
and my hair heavy, older still, with grease.

SARAH SPILLER

Three Stories

Sarah Spiller is a freelance television reporter who has worked for Channel Four and the BBC. She is currently completing her first novel.

Zero Gravitas

Ionce met a man who said he was a curator of space. I remember thinking this an exciting title, admitting many possibilities.

But I never got round to asking him about the full extent of his remit and, in some ways – in these look-towards-the-millennium days – I rather regret that. The alleged curator could have told me a thing or two about our future times. In other ways, though, I treasure my space interface with this person. In a way, he was a star, an omen.

I came across this strangely employed man when I was walking the solar system – or at least a model of it – at the Greenwich Observatory. For a time in my life I used to spend quite a few winter afternoons in this place, wandering from scaled-down planet to planet, space-room to room. It was a black sort of walk, with a few other nobodies there, all doing what I was, marching around trying to fill time.

Oddly for a space curator, the thing that first caught my eye was his T-shirt. He had a rocket going up his stomach.

And the T-shirt provided the opportunity for an opening gambit, a prod of conversation across the void.

"Great T-shirt," I said, as I passed Mars.

The man paused. He didn't get it at first. Then he slowed down on his way to Jupiter.

"Thanks," he nodded and got in step with me. "I got it in Houston."

Thus our meeting proceeded, gravely, and, at that stage, with no allusions to our inhospitable surroundings, the black vortex around us.

"Grand, Jupiter, isn't it?" I said.

"Yes," he replied, "I suppose you could say that."

He paused. "Though, I have heard it said…" He drifted, then resumed, "…that it's large and rather useless."

This took me aback, this distancing ploy, quoting a sour view of a planet to dissuade further contact. I tried to think of a way to re-programme the conversation for expansion.

"But it's big, isn't it? It's The King Of The Gods."

We considered Jupiter together. Him evasive, me trying to hang on to some thread across space.

"Jupiter," he said, "is in fact large enough to hold thirteen hundred Earths. As to its being useless, I suppose we'll never really know why it's there."

He continued, on another train of thought. "But it was from watching Jupiter and four of its twelve moons that the speed of light was determined. So, to a certain extent, it has served a purpose."

We fell silent and I pondered the notion of light years.

This measurement had always seemed to me a hard one to grasp, but it wasn't as if I hadn't thought of it before. I became irritated with the easy-peasy, talking-down tone this man was adopting.

I might not have explored the truths of astrophysics, grappled with its implausible equations, but I was a veteran of the solar system walk. At that time I went most Sundays and could memorise the plaques and leaflets with the best of them.

"Pity there's no life there!" I said, cheery.

And the man flickered a wan smile, and we both got back on course and proceeded to Saturn.

As we walked I snuck a sly look at my watch and calculated how many light years it might take to get to the bus stop and catch the 49 home. I saw I had just ten minutes to brook possible implosion in this black hole of a meeting. I'd have to work swiftly to open this thing out, to poke into a friendlier orbit.

"Walk in space often?" I asked.

"Yes," he said. He stopped walking and looked beyond him. "It makes me find the purpose of being."

It took me a good two minutes to put this one together. This was his kind of a joke. He was middle-aged, he was alluding to some ancient record album.

I thought fast. Then I was able to kick into his mind-set, add an expansive rejoinder.

"My body is walking in space too, " I said. "My soul is in orbit."

He beamed, then suggested that maybe he'd see me again some time.

For the next two weeks I walked to distraction around the solar system. I lingered around Venus and Mercury, traversed the two white caps of Mars and its rust-coloured plains. Cold but exquisite Saturn, sad Uranus, Neptune and Pluto; large, and possibly useless Jupiter.

But I saw no sign of my friend and when I got on the number 49 home after my solar forays, I looked at the night sky and I saw stars that were dead on arrival, frail light that travelled to no end; stars that may have been extinguished millions of years ago, but still appeared, redundant, in the night sky.

I grew depressed with the no-show of my man in the T-shirt. In my mind I took apart our first conversation – my first ever in the solar system – and worried about where I'd gone wrong. I planned how, if we ever met again, I'd lead our observations down different paths.

I read as much as I could. I studied tedious text books and bizarre magazines; I poured over accounts of aliens and crashed UFOs. I was well genned-up for the next time I saw him.

Three weeks passed, then four.

Then, one winter Sunday, I caught sight of him again. Lurking around the Sun.

The Sun was in the end room and I made a rapid calculation that it would be difficult for him to break out further into space very quickly. I had him cornered.

I danced around him in a Copernican circle, then changed direction to creep up on him in an oval ellipse. I moved fast – nothing would admit impediment to my voyage through void. I was a spaceship and he was my star, my ever-fixed mark.

I sidled up and tapped him on the shoulder.

"Good T-shirt," I said.

"Thanks."

He'd replaced the rocket with a picture of Jupiter, which rested on his pot belly.

We moved together towards Mars and I started talking, anxious to fill our silence.

I ruminated on the naming of the planet's two moons Phobias and Deimos, fear and terror. Then I injected a positive note, rehearsing debates about the planet's clouds. I said there were still good reasons for thinking that Mars could be host to primitive life.

He replied that Mars ain't the kind of place to raise your kids; I was able to say that it was cold as hell, having researched ancient vinyl as well as astronomy.

I broadened the conversation to recovered alien bodies, UFOs and other fashionable matters. He listened politely, solemnly and then said that where he worked they took all that weird stuff with a large pinch of salt.

"So where do you work?" I asked.

He looked caught on the hop, a little surprised.

"Space," he said. "I am a curator of space."

For a moment I was dazzled.

There was him in his T-shirt, there was me trotting around burbling my key facts, and there was his ineffable discipline all around us.

I thought hard about selecting a spatially correct line of conversation, but like the first time we'd met, we were sucked into a black hole of our own making. It was as if we were two galaxies crashing into each other, an infinite equation with no beginning and no end. We were a repetition of black, that impossible, that unthinkable.

But as we walked back to the Earth, pausing on the way at the Moon, he started up again, unexpectedly. He scrutinised the lunar landscape, then gestured.

"They took country and western when they went there," he said.

I thought hard. This was a breakthrough.

"I'd take Frankie up there," I said. "Sinatra, doing it his way." I warmed to this new theme. "I'd take someone weightless, with zero gravitas."

He agreed.

He smirked.

He understood!

He came over JFK, he came over grand, he put on a presidential twang. "We shall send to the moon, two-hundred and forty thousand miles away from the control station at Houston, a giant rocket."

I joined in: "We set sail on this new sea, because there is new knowledge to be gained."

He beamed again and we started tottering into orbit.

We cavorted through space, back to Mars, to its possibly thin atmosphere, holding out the possibilities of life. We arrived with a jolt back at Jupiter.

The man's jollity evaporated as he peered at the mirror image of his T-shirt, at Jupiter, the no-hope, no-joke planet. He waited for several minutes before he cleared his throat.

"Of course, technology now sends out different messages," he said. "Things have changed since that first journey to the Moon."

And he proceeded to talk of Hubble, the telescopic eye into the cosmos and what it had shown us of the impact of the Shoemaker-Levy comet on Jupiter: how parts of the large, useless planet had been smashed to smithereens in a random cosmic collision.

"Hubble shows us everything and nothing," he concluded. "Our demise. As we see, so we are expunged."

We continued walking to the outer edges of the solar system. In my head I argued with the man's dismal extrapolation.

"But," I said, tentative, as we neared Uranus, "but –"

"But," I said, my uncertainty, now changing to certainty, now changing to confidence.

"But what of the bankrupt comets which join other fragments in space, the shooting stars? The clusters of particles, falling bursts of light? The Stars you can wish on, the augurs of hope?"

"What you refer to is an omen," he said unhappily. "And an omen," he continued, "is far removed from an understanding."

"I would say that it is a large and useless conceptual nothing amid the possibility, the probability, of an implausible unthinkable conceptual something."

He continued peering at Jupiter, but as I watched him I refused to feel let down. In spite of this man's gloom, I now had a large knowledge of old records and a smattering of useless astronomical trivia.

I had found myself on an untried mission to an unknown celestial body with a stranger whose alleged job description defied small talk, but walking in space I had still made a connection.

We got to Pluto and parted, the man fading into the dark as I boarded the 49.

As the bus crept through the night, I thought that though the pinpricks of light may be dead on arrival, I'd still seen a vain hope against hope stalking the void, an omen.

And though my curator was possibly not one-hundred per cent accurate about his job – though he was quite possibly a charlatan – since meeting this defensive nothing and someone, I feel differently when I look into the night sky now.

If I've any regrets they're of zero gravitas. Too few to mention.

Crazyjet Arrives

Crazyjet arrives on the scene on Friday. Another of her letters.
"How do you people live?" she asks.

"Maybe when I have the baby the four of us can be in the happy home together. You, your husband, me, and the illegitimate child. I'll fly down from Scotland; I'll get an easy jet to Luton."

A cheapie, she calls it. Twenty-nine quid return.

But Crazyjet really has no need for that. She's one ace letter-writer already.

She's having the baby, the uncompleted foetus all on her own. There's no need to fly anywhere to accept her glob, the wet sac plopping onto the blank page. The letters are quite enough, news from nowhere.

Crazyjet writes in the first person, normally.

She tells us she once lectured in International Relations at Harvard. She tells us she's an expert organist (it's a blizzard, her c.v.). She says that she had cancer recently and that the baby, for this reason, may not be viable.

She sends my husband little electronic bleeps about blood tests, tissue tests and scans – to keep us all up to date.

And I've come to love the letters, the news of her glob, the Crazyjet way. I've become involved.

I think of a mouth-organ singing International Relations, the cheapie plane she might have taken to Harvard. The forty per cent chance of survival with 'womb cancer'. (Ovarian? Cervical?)

I think: I'm not musical, though I like a tambourine.

I'm not academic, not even sure of domestic relations, let alone the Cold War.

I've never had cancer, though I have had a foetus, uncompleted, and though I've never tackled my husband on this Crazyjet question, I know she exists.

She must do, a plane-ride away, where I used to live, where I am.

(I've researched it. Crazyjet: Date/Time of attendance, Friday, 10.48, bleeding P.V. since 0945 this am. Lower abdominal pain, 12 weeks, distressed. Passed 200ml clot in A and E, no obvious wet sac. Diagnosis: Spontaneous Abortion).

Getting the latest of her blank sheets this Friday, the baby-girly writing, joined up and curly, I ponder how we could all live, square the circle from Scotland to Herts, just do it.

There is room. Here in Luton.

We could convert a shed, the dog's kennel. We could stick her in the greenhouse, put her out to grass in the paddock. We could all of us sing along together, play instruments, we could all four of us, rub along.

My Husband arrives home this Friday his electronic bleeper singing out news of a spontaneous abortion, his innocent eyes shining out gratitude that at last life is a real mess.

The letters, the miscarriage, her phantom pregnancy. The possibilities of music, the end of the Cold War and, now, an end to it all.

He suggests a cheapie flight to Glasgow from Luton to double-check it further. He wants to Crazyjet up there to make her pee into tests. He says you can't believe a word she writes – from the organ to relations to cancer, which is anorexia, he says.

He gets dramatic. He says he's going to have to watch her on the toilet, buy two different types of test: one Boots; one Clear Blue. (He's researched it.)

We sleep uncomfortably.

I dream and I feel like I'm in the shed, in the dog-house, then like I'm getting hot under my collar in the Greenhouse. Then put out to grass. Put out to moan in the paddock, with some sickness of the womb.

I dream that I feel sad then cross, then anxious, then, suddenly, end-of-the-world happy-clappy with my tambourine. Light and airy and nothing like anything to do with domesticity.

I dream that I'm international in my reach. I'm boarding that cheapie plane to Harvard with my mouth-organ and my glob.

When I wake My Husband's gone up in the air.

When he returns, he reports back.

It's Saturday. He's made notes.

Crazyjet needs help.

She needs The Samaritans, she needs MIND.

She needs specialised advice from the Directory Of Chartered Psychologists. She needs CancerLink and BACUP and the Eating Disorders Association based in Norwich. The Perinatal Bereavement Unit based in London, the Stillbirth and Neonatal Death Society, the Support After Termination For Foetal Abnormality, accessed via a Post Office box. The Miscarriage Association based in West Yorkshire.

She needs all the self-help she can get. There's no sign of a mouth-organ, a tambourine, or any books on international relations in the sheltered accommodation where she lives. There's no sign of the letters. ("Or for that matter," he says, "any kinds of writing materials.")

I ask him about the toilet, the tests: the Boots; the Clear Blue.

"Ha!" he says, "ha." The tell-tale double-blue streaks.

"Nothing in it! Lying! A fantasist!"

"And," I say, "illiterate!"

He smiles approvingly.

Illiterate too. There were no letters, she couldn't string a sentence together if she tried. There was no musical talent for organ or tambourine. There was no keen interest in relations, domestic or otherwise. No foetus completed or uncompleted, no wet sac, no glob. No life, no death, no cancer. She's just rather thin.

It's all news from nowhere, via Crazyjet. We're not all going to live together in the kennel. It's all in the mind, in my mind.

No one stalks anyone's emotions, their hormones, their will. No one enjoys this kind of stuff, it's not allowed. It's a cheapie, it's tabloid, it's unreal. It's illiterate. It's an easy jet, a Crazyjet away.

His eyes shine again with happy doggy devotion. His brown pupils dilate into a pool of unqualified love. His look says it all.

His look this Saturday says: *we're involved*.

Divorce Tour

Mary's lover wants to buy a cold frame between them, a discreet gesture as befits a discreet relationship. They lie in bed as he outlines the cost of the cold frame, the dimensions, what they might grow in it.

His idea is for something around the twenty quid mark, four foot by four, and a rambling melon plant. (He's always wanted to grow an outdoor melon, ever since spying one on a dung heap in Asia, when he was off taking photographs for *National Geographic Magazine*.)

Mary asks him where exactly he posits the cold frame. He tells her it will be placed by the side of his wife's vegetable patch.

"And when the melon plant starts to ramble, you will think of me."

"You have it. The point."

Mary has it, the point. He likes them to be unfussy with each other. He likes precision, being spare with feelings and emotions, expressing what you want clearly, nothing more, nothing less. No spillage.

He looks at his watch, gets dressed, leaving her a cheque for ten quid.

With her friends, Mary rails about him: the normal stuff, women's lives lived on curves of emotions. He should get divorced. She should threaten him, develop some pretty illness, lymph cancer for example. That would show him. She should get pregnant deliberately, have an abortion, a scrape.

Nobody's listening. Everyone else is railing too. Scrapes, pretty illnesses, divorce. From different perspectives, according to differently wronged parties; one crisis always too many, a thousand never enough.

One woman is talking about another woman who's on a divorce tour of Britain. Expecting her friends to lay down their livers and lungs for her future good health. (Greater love hath no woman, than to drink her way through the European wine lake, smoke her way through American tobacco fields for divorcing friends.)

Another woman is talking about another woman, who's coming out of another bad relationship with another lover, who is not divorcing his partner, despite scrapes, pretty illnesses, wine and tobacco.

Mary describes the cold frame idea, the rambling melon, with references to emotions. Cover soil with mulch. When plant has made four true leaves cut off at growing point, just above third leaf. Train tendrils along ground. Hand pollinate flowers to prevent misshapen fruits.

Harvest with half an inch of stalk attached when fully mature.

A rambling melon.

Mary's lover says in lieu of any activity on the cold frame front, he's going out to buy one. He'll put it in place and take photographs of the outdoor melon plant as it grows.

His wife likes the idea of the cold frame too, though clearly does not know it's true purpose, what the rambling melon is all about.

Mary doesn't reply this time. She can't think how to describe what a fucking stupid notion this rambling melon is, without rambling herself. Tendrils! Hand pollinate flowers to prevent misshapen fruits! Harvest!

It is absurd and he knows it. Mary has it. The point.

There are endless photographs of this exercise. After the cold frame has been purchased – ten quid each – the soil is prepared for the mulch. (Photograph one. The mulch.) The fragile shoot is then put in place. (Photograph two. The original plant.) Then the tendrils start to appear. (Photograph three. The tendrils.)

They lie in bed surveying these pictures, as he describes the progress of the rambling melon, how a second pruning has become necessary.

Mary loves him, but the business of loving him is unbearable. It rambles around her brain, attaches itself to her daily actions (brushing her teeth, combing her hair, trying to keep it all together at work).

She loves him and she thinks she can smell it. It has a rich fruity fragrance.

The woman on the divorce tour of Britain has developed a terminal disease without intending to. It is not pretty and it is not even a threat to any errant male lover. It is an illness which will stay there inside her and cannot, unusually, be talked about.

It has no relation to men. Words can't describe it, nothing gets close to the terror of death, the smell, the fear of it. It is rotten luck.

The illness rambles around this woman's body and nothing can stop the cancer cells dividing, sub-dividing, taking over. The tendrils of pain, misshapen breasts, no breasts maybe. (They will have to come off, though it's probably too late.)

It's gone to her liver and lungs somehow, despite the divorce tour.

Or maybe because of the divorce tour. Maybe that's how it started.

Photographs seven, eight and nine show the melon plant filling the cold frame.

But Mary wants to lie there in bed with her lover being greedy with this gorgeous melon. She wants them to pass the melon from mouth to mouth, tongue to tongue as they make love.

She wants to put the melon inside her. She wants him to taste both her and the melon. Christ. She wants him to leave his wife, move in with her. She wants to give up work and have dozens of children, hundreds, thousands of his children. She wants the lot.

Happy home, garden, cold frame.

She wants it, but she can't have it. This is the point. The melon will only ever appear in the photographs. (Appearances will be kept up, discretion is key. It's essential.)

Scrapes, illnesses, pretty and terminal, whatever. Whatever Mary might think of doing, he won't allow spillage. It's simply not part of this game plan. He has posited the cold frame where it is, he has posited the melon, and he hates her rambling on about emotions.

It's his joke.

Mary's not even married but she's going on her own divorce tour. She loves him but she has to leave him, even if it's terminal.

She has to leave the bloody photographs, the cold frame, even the rambling melon. Its possibilities.

The idea that one day she might eat it.